22

NEW WORLD WRITING

22

NEW
WORLD
WRITING

J. B. LIPPINCOTT COMPANY
Philadelphia & New York

Grateful acknowledgment is made to Chappell & Co., Inc., for permission to quote from the lyrics of "The Lady Is a Tramp," copyright © 1937 by Chappell & Co., Inc., New York, N.Y.

CONTENTS

22

NEW WORLD WRITING

MICHAEL SHURTLEFF
The Lady Is a Tramp, Geraldine

I.

Geraldine had stuffed her brain with cotton wool and she wore a heavy black sleeping mask over her eyes and she was buried deep in her bed with the heavy Wisconsin patchwork quilt wound around her head and she dreamed determinedly that she was in a land of peace and quiet, but still Buddy Greco won the battle. She gets too hungry for dinner at eight, she likes the opera but never comes late. Right in her ear. As if he were bending over and shouting it right to her: that's why that's why that's why the lady is a tramp. Oh, stereo.

Buddy Greco, I hate you, said Geraldine and tried to burrow deeper into her nest. But it was no good. He followed her wher-

MICHAEL SHURTLEFF is a playwright whose *Call Me by My Rightful Name* was successfully produced in New York two seasons ago and "drew rousing newspaper salutes for its author," to quote *Time* Magazine. A play version of "The Lady Is a Tramp, Geraldine" appeared last season at New York's Theatre de Lys, along with two other Shurtleff one-act plays: *So It's All Rashomon* and *A Baker's Dozen*. Mr. Shurtleff has recently completed a novel, *Happy New Year Gregorio*. His new full-length play, *I Hate to See a Party End*, is scheduled for production this spring in London and next fall on Broadway.

ever she went. So she rolled out of bed and onto the floor, since there was no other way to get out of that twist of comforters and quilts she had built during the night to protect herself against this very onslaught. Dear Lord, she said as she crawled on her hands and knees trailing blankets and clouds of glory, dear Lord, don't you take care of mothers on Christmas Day, too? Why is it just for the little ones and for savage beasts. For Juanita was a savage beast. Dear Lord, I hate Buddy Greco but I hate Juanita more. Stereo go bragh.

She bumped into the folding French doors with her head, just like a Minnesota buffalo. With this setback she huddled in her distraught blankets and prayed in her fashion, first for patience to deal with the world of noise, which meant Juanita and Buddy Greco, and second to stave off the world of Howard Johnson. It's Christmas for me, too, J.C., she complained in her hut of comforters. Oh, le bon dieu, it's supposed to be for all of us. Not just for my darling children.

And with prayer behind her, she crept on all fours from her little partition she referred to, laughingly of course, as her bedroom, and into the living room, where Howsmer, age eight, was running his new electric train around and around the Christmas tree, and Charlotte, age eleven, was sorting through her new phonograph records with a loud and continuous chanting singsong, for Charlotte was in the midst of a Sing Along phase. But the real culprit was still Buddy Greco, louder than any train, louder than any sing-along girl, and the constant companion of Miss Juanita.

"Look at Mother!" said Charlotte to Howsmer, thinking Geraldine must be up to some Christmas morning diversion.

"What the hell is she now?" said Juanita.

"Mommy's a Christmas morning water buffalo," said Geraldine, finally finding a way to stick her head out of the trailing covers, "and you," she said directly to Juanita, "you are a damned——"

"Not in front of the children!" said Juanita, stretching her silky sexy legs from underneath her pink and ruffly shortie gown. Buddy went into a particularly vibrant thumping section of his song that made Geraldine crumple on the floor with a moan.

"This is a very fine selection," said Charlotte, as Howsmer

shifted from attention to his train to a sudden thunder of drum-beats. Geraldine moaned again to realize that Juanita had defi-nitely and defiantly given Howsmer that drum for Christmas, thereby destroying peace forever in her household.

"She can't hear you, darling," said Juanita to Charlotte.

"Can't hear me?" said Howsmer, pounding louder.

"She can't hear you, darling," said Juanita to Howsmer, ges-ticulating to her ears. "Plugs," Juanita said, in an elaborate pan-tomine to indicate Geraldine's ears were stopped up, and arti-ficially, too, and with added flourishes to indicate Geraldine was not all right in the head department, anyhow.

"I'd have to be dead and buried not to hear!" said Geraldine, bursting forth from her blanketed cocoon and descending on Juanita with pure murder in her eyes. "I told you Juanita: no drums! I begged you: no drums!" She had her long and strong fingers around Juanita's neck.

"Darling—kids have got to have what they want on Christmas —oh, my throat—even if parents——" Juanita would talk her way even unto death. Geraldine kept pushing her fingers around that pretty little neck, that sensuous stamen or pistil or stalk, whatever the hell it was, it was a definite pleasure to be throttling it, for if there was no life in her neighbor lady, then there might be peace and sleep and quiet and sleep for Geraldine, who was deserving.

"I've never seen you purple before," said Geraldine, not relax-ing her fingers for a moment. "It's very becoming."

"Oh—oh—pul-lease," said Juanita, starting to go under. "Not —not in front of the children—not murder——"

"You ought to try purple as your next All-Over Basic Make-up Color," said Geraldine, "if you live through this——"

"Please, Geraldine, darling——"

"—which I doubt you will," said Geraldine, grinding her teeth together in the pleasure of killing Juanita on Christmas morning. Ah, what freedom, what a lovely sacrificial lamb. God's in his heaven and all's quiet with the world because Juanita is dead at last."

"It really hurts!" said Juanita, jerking like a hollyhock.

Geraldine let go as suddenly as she had started and she swatted

Juanita on the behind. "You haven't got a stitch on!"

"Really, Geraldine," said Juanita, very blond and very pouty and rubbing at her neck in her best Brigitte pose, "you'll make them into sexual puritans and perverts, the way you carry on!"

"Go put on something decent!" Geraldine grabbed her by the hair and the buttocks and propelled the Lady Juanita into her own side of the house, virtually tossing her through the open French doors. "I won't raise my children with the sight of your bare ass wiggling in front of their faces on the Lord's Day!"

"The Lord's Day!" mocked Juanita.

"Or any other day!" said Geraldine.

"The Lord's Day!" Juanita was enchanted with it. "Where'd you learn to talk like that, Jane Darwell?" She leaned against her own set of French doors and leered at Geraldine.

"And turn off Buddy Greco," said Geraldine plaintively. "Would you? For a little while?"

Geraldine kneeled and kissed each of her children and wished them a Merry Christmas. She was very lavish with her affection, being an outgoing lady, as she frequently had cause to rue, and her children were in turn fond of her. Not without problems fond, but still fond.

"You know as well as I do," said Juanita, "that Christmas has nothin' to do with the Lord. It's just a nice commercial holiday so we can have a day off and spend all our hard-earned money."

"Hard-earned?" said Geraldine, a trifle bitterly. "Your money hard-earned?"

"The Lord probably never even heard of Christmas," said Juanita.

"Do not take the Lord's name in vain," said Charlotte, more by rote than out of primness.

Geraldine gave Charlotte an extra kiss. "That's right, darling," and she looked triumphantly at Juanita.

"In vain," said Howsmer, and Geraldine kissed him, too.

"That's right, darling," she said.

"That's right, darling," said Howsmer. Geraldine looked at him suspiciously for a moment, but he seemed engrossed in his trains again—having put aside the drums, thank the Good Lord, no matter whose day it was—and seemed further to have meant no particular satire of her. Geraldine reasoned that you could never be sure, with children.

Juanita was in her side of the house, changing from her nylon shortie into nylon slacks (Geraldine thought it wasn't much of an improvement, but everything Juanita owned seemed diaphanous), and muttering, "The Lord's Day indeed," over and over to herself until it became a chant.

"Listen, Mrs. Popocatypetal," said Geraldine, picking up in her side of the house, "Don't slander us with your irreligious gospel."

"I'm just honest," said Juanita proudly. "You Bible-bitten bitches"—she corrected herself, with a glance at the children—"biddies are always against honesty."

Geraldine picked up snow suits and mittens and gloves and socks and newspapers and orange peelings and didn't say a word, so Juanita followed her. "I am not irreligious," said Juanita, "I just don't think God has to be catered to."

"I don't disagree with that," said Geraldine, who had the uneasy feeling Juanita had picked the phrase up from her. It didn't sound right coming from Juanita. "But you are irreligious." Juanita made one of her sounds of total disbelief. "There's nothing in all this world," said Geraldine, folding up the blankets in her own little corner of the world, "more irreligious than an ex-Catholic—especially a streetwalker."

"My," said Juanita, "you did get out of the wrong side of the bed."

Geraldine pushed Juanita aside to finish repairing her tiny slice of bedroom. "If I could have wakened naturally," she said grimly, "instead of to the insane caucauphony of that Buddy Greco——"

"You two have to fight on Christmas morning?" said Charlotte, with just the slightest shade of disapproval.

"We're just discussing," said Geraldine, giving a dirty look at Juanita as if it were all her fault. Geraldine rustled her fingers through Charlotte's hair and stood sighing at the mysteries of her daughter.

"Every time you rustle Charlotte's hair," said Juanita, "doesn't suddenly turn you into a model mother, dear." She walked suavely up to Geraldine and cracked her across the face with her scarlet-nailed and dexterous hand. "Don't call me a streetwalk-er!" she screamed, and jerked the sleep mask from right off the top of Geraldine's head, where it had been perched like a tiny bat.

Geraldine cracked Juanita right back. "Then don't act like one!" she said and marched into her bedroom slice before they could hit each other again. Juanita did some marching, too, right past the children, into her own quarters, slamming the French doors behind her until the glass vibrated like fine violin strings in the Christmas air.

"Good riddance to bad rubbish!" said Geraldine, more to her-self than anyone else and because she needed the final word after that earthquaking door slammed the duplex house into the halves it was meant to be.

"Bad rubbish," said Howsmer, proving that in her household it was impossible to talk to yourself.

"Ssh, Howsmer," said Charlotte, "let them fight it out."

"Fight it out," said Howsmer acceptingly.

"You will learn," said the sage Charlotte, "that a gentleman never interferes in a fight between two ladies."

Geraldine finished making up her bed and pushed it up into the wall so it could pretend not to be a bed. "Not if he values his life he won't," she said, in agreement with her daughter's advice.

"Values his life," said Howsmer, and for a moment Geraldine thought he was giving this idea a really good mull, but in a moment he went back to his train, staring at it with the intensity of an empire builder. She took him in her arms because she couldn't resist doing it, for she lived, as all mothers do, in that area whereby she might at any moment be totally rejected for the possibility of treating her offspring like an infant.

"Value your life, darling," she said to him. "No one else ever will." She rocked him back and forth on her haunches and then, seeing Charlotte, she sighed. "That's no philosophy for a Christ-mas morning."

"Nor for any morning," added Charlotte.

Geraldine let her son slip away while she fixed her eye on her daughter. "Are you always right, Miss Prim?"

"Nearly always," said Charlotte, reading a dust jacket.

"Nearly," said Howsmer absently, or was it so absently?

"Where'd you get that idea?" Geraldine asked Charlotte.

"You said so yourself."

"I make mistakes all the time," said the all-too-human Geraldine, getting up and pushing back the folding French doors so that her bedroom alcove began to disappear and with it, Geraldine sometimes thought, all proof that she had any life of her own. Was it really such a comfort to see that it was now all living room instead of living room with a hunk bitten out for a bed? Yes, she told herself, setting her shoulders squarely, it was, it was.

"Do you think I should go more blond or less?" Juanita had re-entered, comb and brush in hand.

"I think it's too late," said Geraldine.

Juanita stared in the mirror, putting her head to one side, then the other. "I think more blond looks more natural, don't you?"

"More blond is more natural. . . ." Geraldine shook her head, feeling a little old, feeling all too much suddenly as if she were Juanita's mother instead of her contemporary. "Sure." She briskly hit the pillows on the sofa. "Sure, kid. More blond is more natural."

"You think I don't know what nature is, dontcha?"

"I thought you got mad and went home."

"This is my home," said Juanita. She pointed to Geraldine's side of the house with a sweep of her hand. "That's my home," pointing to her own side of the duplex. "It's all my home," she said, regal as a queen. "I own it all."

Geraldine wanted to tell her to shut up but she settled for a groan.

"Yes, again, missus," said Juanita, punishing her. "On account of for your benefit, you need to be told."

"Like a hole in the head, Mrs. Pandemonium."

"And," said Juanita, even more insistently, "I own the garage and I own the car in it."

"And the key in the car—that's yours, too."

Juanita shot her a suspicious look, as if Geraldine had something below the belt in mind. So she added, "And another thing,

I'm not saddled with two kids, either, makin' me old before my time."

Your time, your time indeed, thought Geraldine, the time is always now for an addlepated girl who doesn't have to bother with growing up. "I'm not *saddled* with my children, Mrs. Bumpkin Llewellyn-Jones. I happen to love them and want them."

"Huh," was all Juanita could think of to say to that. After all, mother love was pretty frightening and irrefutable. Besides, Juanita loved the damn kids herself. But the damage was done. Howsmer dropped the caboose on the train and ran to Geraldine, burying his nose in her pajamas so firmly that she could feel the sobs starting clear through her thighs. She gave Juanita a now-see-what-you've-done look and gathered Howsmer cheerfully into her arms.

Juanita wanted to help, too. She held her arms out to Howsmer, as if it were all Geraldine's fault, for she was convinced that was the case; wasn't it always? "Howsmer, honey, come here to your Auntie Juanita." He cried only the louder. "Whenever you're home," Juanita shot at Geraldine, "nobody can do a thing with him. Howsmer, honey."

"You are not his aunt," said Geraldine.

"You're his mother," said Juanita, every bit as if Geraldine were not.

"Now what do you mean by that remark, Mrs. Red Hot Hips——"

"Missus, please!" Juanita held up the red claws and shook her head in lovely mock distress. "Not in front of the kiddies. Please."

Geraldine thought she would belt her one and then she thought, no, a mother has to have control no matter how provoking the landlady is; she'd settle for giving Juanita a good old-fashioned shaking. Instead she reasoned with Howsmer, for he was more important than revenge. She held him in the crook of her arm and she said very matter of factly, "Howsmer, how can a boy of your imagination and your inspiration cry on Christmas Day? A boy with your know-how." He stopped sniveling and was listening. "Christmas Day," she went on. "Just think: Christmas Day, Howsmer. You got a train, you got the darn drums—"

she chuckled, taking him in on the conspiracy—"you got the darn drums in spite of, didn't you? You got a lovely tree, you got Charlotte, you got me."

"I got you," said Howsmer, and Geraldine was filled with Thanksgiving and Christmas and every other holiday of the year as well as tears in her eyes and a resolution to forgive Juanita no matter what she did. She and Howsmer hugged each other, Geraldine held back her sniffles and then she gave him a sweet little smack on the behind and said, "Off you go." She stood up, wiping her eyes surreptitiously, as Howsmer went back to his train.

She turned to Juanita with a look of commiseration and Juanita begrudgingly had to give in, the way they always did with one another. "Well, missus," said Juanita, "you got a way with the words."

"I got a way with the heart," said Geraldine, who never felt as strong with the words as she'd like to have been.

"Still, I think," said Juanita, getting all over languid again, "that a truly permissive environment would give him a tongue of his own."

Geraldine's shoulders slumped; it took just those words, just a pin to prick the balloon of good feeling, and Juanita just couldn't resist doing it. Lord forgive her, said Geraldine to the Lord, for she's oversexed and knows not what she does. Maybe having a tongue of your own wasn't the best thing in the world, when you saw the uses people put it to. Still, that was a choice her son should have for himself, and this way . . . Geraldine wanted to cry for Howsmer, but she had done this too many times in the past already; she was beginning to suspect she was crying not for him but for herself, so crying was hereafter to be disallowed. No matter what unkind thing Juanita thought she must say in the name of honesty. So Geraldine held her head high and started a good Christmas hum of her own as she set about the tasks a mother has to face on Christmas Day. Especially a mother who has to be father as well; maybe it was having to play both roles that got her down. Being a breadwinner and a housewife and a mother and a father—it was too many roles, even for a lady whose outlook was always on the jolly side. Hum, hum, hum brightly, Geraldine told herself, and went into a rousing rendition of "Hark the Herald Angels Sing" through her nose.

"All this talk," said Juanita. And when no one asked her what talk, she said: "All this talk of propriety you're always puttin' on —you sure them kids ever had a father?"

Geraldine went from humming to singing the words right out loud: Joy to all the congregation! Who brought in this litigation! Hark the herald angels sing! (Oh, she never could remember words and always had to write words of her own. Why did words have to make sense when there was a lovely tune to carry them along? Rhyme should be enough.)

"Where'd you ever learn a word like permissive?" she asked Juanita, as she started things going in the kitchen alcove. Some day she would have a house without a single alcove. Nothing but good full rooms all over the place.

"You like to think I don't know nothin'," said Juanita.

"Oh, you know about sex, all right."

"Well, I guess you did, too, once upon a time," said Juanita brightly right back, "or were those both immaculate conceptions?"

Geraldine laughed.

"So there was a father?"

"You know there was."

"I ain't never seen him." Juanita swung her sexy legs smoothly to and fro, to and fro, just like the ticktock thing that used to sit on her piano teacher's desk.

"I haven't seen him myself in a good long time."

"So? Tell me about him."

"I've told you about him."

"So I forget. Tell me again."

Geraldine sang some more phrases of "Hark the Herald Angels Sing" and then she started in as if she were telling a bedtime story: "He was an aerialist in the circus. A great star of the air. The Great Whatoozie! You must have heard of him, Juanita, even you: everyone in the world heard of The Great Whatoozie! He was proud and arrogant—a beautiful figure of a man. Just the right proportion of muscle and bone—not an ounce of excess flesh on him. He was taut as a wire, all the time. He moved like a panther, with a panther's sinewy grace, with a panther's kingly feeling over all the world. . . ." Geraldine stood still with half an orange in each hand, drinking in the thought of what it must be like to be king of all the world.

"I want tomato juice, please," said Charlotte, who had been listening to all of this and was just a little bit frightened by it.

"You got some imagination, Geraldine," said Juanita. "I got to hand you that."

"So has Charlotte Russe," said Geraldine, putting a hand on her daughter's head. "And so has Howsmer," and she put a hand on her son's head. "It's the thing that counts most in all this world. Humor—and imagination. Reality—bah, that's easy. *You* got reality, Mrs. Blondine. You got it, you keep it, lovely."

"It pays the bills," said Juanita, with the smugness of the irrevocable. "You shoulda married an artist, not a traveling salesman."

"But orange juice," Geraldine was explaining to Charlotte, "real orange juice! Not special frozen, but real squoze, special real orange juice for Christmas Day!"

"Tomato juice is the right color," said Charlotte.

"You drink this now," said Geraldine, wondering why when tomato juice was easier, "and we'll have tomato juice as a cocktail before dinner, eh?"

"You think I'm easy to pacify," said Charlotte and smiled at her mother. Charlotte had a way of saying the truth that would make you want to hit most kids, but Charlotte always seemed to forgive you for what she knew. Dear Charlotte Russe. If only she wouldn't keep getting brighter and brighter; her IQ was beginning to show all over the place and that wasn't good for a girl.

"You—easy?" said Geraldine. "You're not easy, you're too precocious!"

Charlotte took an orange juice and brought it to Howsmer. "Why does everyone hate precocious children?" She watched him speculatively as he drank his juice. "People should be glad," she went on. "But they'd rather have a kid to feel sorry for, wouldn't they?"

Geraldine stood stock still for a moment, her eyes filling with tears, in spite of all her resolutions of bravery. She nearly knocked the orange juice squeezer into the sink, her heart ready to Christmas break over her strange little son. She looked quickly at Juanita, who was being simpatico again, and then she looked away, dabbing at her eyes with the towel so the kids wouldn't see. Both women stood still for a moment, leaning over the sink; then Juanita gave Geraldine a little pat on the shoulders and said, "I'll go flip the disk." So then Geraldine felt free, and Juanita let her complain once more about Buddy Greco before she didn't put the record on.

"Maybe," said Juanita, shrugging easily and giving Geraldine an encouraging tap on the ankle, "it wouldn't have done you no good to have married a artist. After all, look at me." Geraldine looked at her; Juanita was good to look at, no matter how she messed with herself, there was no denying that. "I mean, I got everything," Juanita said, and who could deny that, either? "I got a housea my own, I got a garagea my own, I got a cara my own, I got alimonya my own—and what do I do? I let out half of what's mine, not because I need the money even, but because I gotta have people around me. People. A screw-loose dame who don't know what side her bread is buttered on and two kids one of 'em a genius and the other a nut and between them they don't know when to come in outa the rain. Now why do I like you, Geraldine? Can you tell me that? It don't figure. But I do."

"I'm lovable," said Geraldine, winking.

"Oh, don't wink at me," said Juanita. "I know you're lovable. Just why do I got to be the one that loves you?"

"Howsmer is not a nut, Juanita," said Charlotte, very softly, very certainly, very definitely.

Juanita looked startled, then hurt, then conciliatory. "I didn't mean in no bad sense, baby," she said, bending down. "I just meant like you know: somea your best friends are nuts. You know how people say that, Charlotte Russe."

"Just be careful how you say it," said Charlotte politely.

"Okay, baby." Juanita looked at Geraldine and shrugged.

And Geraldine shrugged right back at her and said: "How can you say you got everything when everything you got's in Queens?"

"You don't like Queens, then move," said Juanita. "Long

Island's a big place, but probably no place on it good enough for you, huh, Duchess? So move."

"Sure," said Geraldine affably.

"You don't like being a hostess at Howard Johnson," said Juanita, "go be a buyer at Saks Fifth Avenue."

Geraldine laughed. "I been thinking," she said.

"That's your trouble," Juanita told her. "All the time thinking. Like one of them god-damn intellectuals."

"No," said Geraldine, laughing again. Juanita was a card today. Geraldine got provoked with her, could hit her, could murder her, but could not resist her. Salt-of-the-earth Juanita: it was impossible to approve of her, impossible to ignore her, impossible not to be engulfed by her. She was just plain impossible.

"Well, your husband was," Juanita said.

"Yep, that he was. A traveling salesman who was an intellectual." Geraldine shook her head over the wonders of America. "Now he said I was a god-damn mother-earth type. And that men with minds are always drawn to earth mothers but earth mothers are the doom of men with minds, so he had to run, flee, screaming through the banshee night to get away from me. . . ."

"On account you were his doom," said Juanita, familiarly.

Geraldine nodded. "On account I was his doom." She wiped away a tear or two, then laughed at herself. Today was sure-tear day.

"Why don't you peel an onion?" asked Juanita.

"Can't stand good honest sentiment, can you?"

"I'm modern."

And Geraldine shook her head if this is what modern was and felt no regrets at being an old-fashioned girl. Or did she? Being old-fashioned didn't seem to pay off except in telling yourself how good you were; nobody else told you anything.

"Let me fix it," said Charlotte, but Howsmer pulled the engine away from her and banged it against the wall. "That's not intelligent, Howsmer," said Charlotte in her reasonable voice. "To destroy something you like."

Geraldine couldn't help but agree but couldn't help but wish Charlotte didn't have to say such reasonable things. It made one want to be so unreasonable. She would have banged the engine against the wall, too, so when Howsmer started to cry and rushed to her, Geralidne couldn't summon up disapproval.

"May I have a cookie, Mother?" asked Charlotte.

"Diversionary tactics?" asked Geraldine, but Charlotte just nodded, took a chocolate cookie from the tin on the sideboard, and held it out to Howsmer, saying she was sorry. But sorrow was not enough. Howsmer took the cookie and threw it across the room. I'd have done that, too, thought Geraldine, and wondered if she could be a good mother and have such an anarchistic thought. After all, Charlotte was right; and she wasn't even piggy about being right. Geraldine rescued the cookie and handed it back to Howsmer, who smiled at her gratefully and ate it.

"Well, sibling rivalry," said Charlotte philosophically.

"Sometimes," Geraldine told her, "I need to feel like the mother."

"I can't," said Charlotte, remarkably for her, "be expected to understand everything." She bent over, rooting in the hall closet now.

"She understands too much, that's her problem," said Juanita.

"You're too good pointing out what other people's troubles are," said Geraldine, watching Charlotte at her closet search. Finally Charlotte confessed she could not find Howsmer's other boot. Geraldine was glad to be of service but a little apologetic about letting Charlotte see where the boot was, holding up the Christmas tree stand. When she fished it out and handed it to Charlotte, the tree leaned a little and became the leaning tower of Christmas Pisa. She was puzzled as she watched Charlotte getting her brother dressed for the out-of-doors, so she chatted to Juanita, who was painting her toenails a special Christmas scarlet.

"I don't know why I'm gaining weight," said Geraldine. "I split right out of my slacks. Why should I gain weight? All I do is stand on my feet at Howard Johnson's eight hours a day and then come here and work eight hours a day and I hardly eat anything and I'm still gaining weight." If Juanita said, You were meant to be fat, she would brain her with the big frying pan, Christmas or children or not.

"Earth mother," said Juanita, and Geraldine picked up the

frying pan but when she turned around Juanita was, of all places, in her own part of the house. So Geraldine told herself it wasn't fair, it wasn't fair at all, she was still a young woman.

"You're a good-looking kid," said Juanita, coming back in with her nail file. "If you'd lose some weight."

Brain her, brain her now. Instead, ask: "But why do I gain it?" and why was Charlotte dressing her brother on Christmas morning. Were they planning to run away, desert her on the day of days, after she'd tried so hard?

"Earth mother," said Juanita again. Now that she'd learned the term—via that ex-husband of Geraldine's, via Geraldine, who already rued it—she wasn't going to give it up without plenty mileage.

"Shut up, please, Mrs. Luciano."

"You resent it on account I married a Puerto Rican."

Geraldine had a hard time following that one. Used as she was to Juanita's non sequiturs, it was ever fascinating to stumble into the trap of a new one.

"I do?"

Juanita nodded. "Uh-huh."

"I never even met the man."

"You resent Puerto Ricans. Even if you don't meet them."

Now where did she get a concept like this? I'm one of the country's most liberal, fair-minded and tolerant ladies, said Geraldine to herself, the only things I don't like are stupid people and people who interfere, and then it doesn't matter what color they are or where they pray. She took the frozen goose out of the refrigerator and saw it had not thawed at all through the night and then remembered the last thing she was supposed to do last night before crawling into her murphy was to put the goose out. She dropped it in the sink and the sound was like a small Hiroshima.

"Be careful," warned Juanita, "you'll crack my sink."

Geraldine smiled at Juanita as if all her teeth ached.

"You should have taken it out last night," said Juanita. Geraldine just let her smile freeze until she felt akin with the goose. She thought for a moment of climbing in the sink with him.

"I know that," she said grimly, thinking why was it the success-

ful people insisted upon telling everyone else such obvious
things, without ever imparting the secrets of their success. Or was
it just the nature of successful people to be irritating to the rest
of us?

"It just takes overnight to thaw out," said Juanita, "*if* you set
it out."

"I know that, thank you, Mrs. Spiegelbach."

"Who's Mrs. Spiegelbach?" asked Juanita, and Geraldine congratulated herself on diversionary tactics. Sometimes it was easier
to handle Juanita than the children.

"Aha," she said, "That's one on you, isn't it? Mrs. Spiegelbach
was my German teacher in college. She tended toward literalism,
too."

"You don't like the Spics, you don't like the Jews, you don't
even like the Germans——"

"Where do you get that insane inventory?"

Juanita sniffed. "It's them what talk so broad-minded what
ain't."

"Where'd you read that?"

"Oh, I did." Juanita was playing the role of the intellectual
seductress now. Whatever layers she added, her basic characteri-
zation was always seductress. Geraldine often wondered what
Juanita's life might have been had she never seen Bardot.

"Along with 'permissive environment'?" Geraldine's voice was
ironic and amused. She may have prayed to have Juanita out
from underfoot, and yet her insane logistics and her involuted
rationalizations added freshness and humor to what might otherwise be many a draggy day. "You know, Juan, it's not enough to
read—you're supposed to *understand,* too."

Charlotte and Howsmer were all dressed and seemed to be
headed for the great world out-of-doors. Without time to decide
if it was truly permissive to ask questions, Geraldine did. "But,
Charlotte Russe, I'm just making breakfast," she said.

"We're invited out to Christmas breakfast, Mother," said Charlotte, in her I-don't-mind-at-all-explaining voice. "To Anna
Maria's. Did you forget?"

"I thought," said Geraldine, "we'd all have Christmas breakfast here. Together."

"We'll all have Christmas dinner together, Mother."

"If it ever thaws," said Juanita.

Charlotte gave her mother a kiss, and then Geraldine bent down to give Howsmer a kiss and a last-minute extra wrap to his muffler.

"We won't be long," said Charlotte, and they exited to a skeptical Juanita, shaking her head, and to a rather woebegone Geraldine, wondering how togetherness works anyhow. Charlotte stuck her head back in: "You can get all that sex talk over with now."

Geraldine turned back to the sink, tossing over her shoulder to Juanita, "You see what a disastrous influence you have on my children."

"Howsmer's the child. You're the child," said Juanita, sipping at the extra orange juice. "Charlotte Russe is the mother."

Geraldine examined the silly gross goose. "We always had goose at Christmas in Mayberry." She ran the hot water over the rocky animal.

"Hot water will make it tough," said Juanita. "Put it in cold. Where's Mayberry?"

"Mayberry, Wisconsin. Where I was raised."

"Oh, yeah." Juanita looked vague. "Wisconsin." One could imagine in her mind's eye that Easterner's idea of a map of the United States, with a little section out near Alaska called Wisconsin. "It's hard to remember anybody ever came from there."

"Why?"

"Wisconsin." Juanita slid it around on her teeth and it wouldn't fit. "Just the sound of it, you know? Wisconsin. Like I mean, where is it? Where can it possibly be?"

"I wish I were there now."

"No, you don't."

"You're right. I don't." Still, Geraldine, lost in the spirit of Christmas, couldn't help nostalgia. "It's just—at Christmas time —my father was such a comfort. And, well, looking around at this little mess of a house, I get homesick. Two kids and work, work, work. It just doesn't add up to a family."

"Not even a little friendly screwing on the side, eh?"

Geraldine turned off the nostalgia and turned the reality back on quick; no one could do it with more of a jolt than dear Juanita. "Charlotte was right," she said, hustling the dishes into the sink.

"Charlotte's always right," Juanita agreed. "What you need is —some whammy." Geraldine looked tortured by this invasion of a woman's privacy. "Well, you do!" Juanita pursued. "Now when Mr. Calcimine gets here——"

"Mr. Kalzamen," corrected Geraldine.

"—don't be so standoff. He's a nice-enough-lookin' fella!"

"I know he is." Now, Juanita, why don't you keep your sexy little nose out of my sexual affairs, because they are botched up enough without any help from you, please.

"You don't like him on account he's Jewish," Juanita decided.

"Nonsense."

"It's true."

"Absolute nonsense." Geraldine found this insistence of Juanita the most exasperating by far; it was even worse than her insistent sexuality; it must be related to it in some way. Geraldine drew on reason to explain, once more. "Juanita: my husband was Jewish. Do you remember that? My grandfather was half-Jewish. I got nothing against anybody in all this world who's Jewish. Or who's Puerto Rican. Or who's Negro. Or who's anything. Why do you keep saying nutty things like that?"

"Why else you leading this virgin life?"

"Oh," said Geraldine, and she sat down, so relieved to learn at last what was behind all this.

"And you don't like minorities. You——"

"The only minority I don't like is you," said Geraldine breezily.

"That's because I was married to a Spic," Juanita shot back, as if Geraldine had fallen right into a carefully prepared trap.

"I thought your husband was Puerto Rican," said Geraldine, puzzled again at the turn of Juanita's mind.

"Same," said Juanita, scornfully. "And because I sometimes date with the dinge."

"The who?"

"Negroes."

"I don't object to Negroes. I told you that. Where'd this crazy idea come from?"

"Homer says——"

"Oh, Homer." Geraldine put these two pieces together. Homer was Juanita's friend and Geraldine did not approve of Homer and therefore it meant Geraldine did not approve of Negroes and ——"Homer does not work. Homer takes money from you. It's not because Homer is a Negro." She spoke very reasonably, but she knew she was up against it this time; you can't win on the colored question, no matter how reasonable you are.

"Homer is a good lay, so I pay him," said Juanita. "That so wrong?"

Geraldine considered it. "I guess not. Not if it doesn't bother either of you."

"Don't bother me none. Like I say, he's a good lay. There ain't so many around, Miss Geraldine."

Geraldine smiled. "I know."

"I'll bet you was a heller when you was young."

"I'm not old!"

"No, you're not. Fine figger of a woman, just like your Mr. Calcimine says. Just lose a little weight."

Geraldine sighed and patted her buttocks. Nice idea, she agreed. She got down on her hands and knees to get the living room in order; it wasn't going to be easy with an electric train running all over the floor.

"What you need is a man, honey," said Juanita, and Geraldine knew she was in for it. "You're like a bitch in heat, I swear, snappin' at everybody. I know the signs. What the hell you holdin' off for? Have a little fun. Why, that Mr. Calcimine looks like one fine roll in the hay. What's the matter, why don't you roll with him? You ain't the primster type, missus; you ain't fooling no one acting so proper, it just ain't in you. You like a good stray in the straw, I know your type, and there ain't nothing wrong with it. Just because you're a mother and you had a son-uvabitch husband who deserted you, does that mean you gotta give up sex? It ain't natural. And what's more, there's nobody askin' that of you, honey, not in 1962, not in Queens, New York, no sirree, this ain't no Mayberry, Wisconsin; here we go around the mayberry tree, no ifs, ands or buts about it. It just ain't nat-

ural for a good juicy woman like you holdin' back all that, turning you into a crank before your time. Now you listen to me,
don't just turn away and put that preach-like look on your face,
you take yourself in hand and let yourself go. . . ."

II.

It was late when they finished dinner, for Geraldine wanted to
be sure the goose had finally lost his frozen interior and so she
had cooked it slowly and for a long, long time. Mr. Kalzamen had
carved it beautifully, though, and if Geraldine thought it still
tasted a bit frozen even after all the hours in the oven, the children ate the exotic bird as if there were nothing wrong and Mr.
Kalzamen was all compliments. He sat now on the sofa, watching
Howsmer taking soldier after soldier from the brilliantly colored
boxes to make a vast battlefield of the living-room floor, while
on the other side of the tree, Charlotte was putting together the
pieces of what promised to be the largest jigsaw puzzle anyone
had ever seen. Between the battlefield and the pieces of the
puzzle, Geraldine had a gingerly time clearing the table. Mr.
Kalzamen said something but Juanita had Buddy Greco singing
"Something's Got to Give" from her side of the house and somehow Buddy had kept getting louder and louder and now she
couldn't hear what Mr. Kalzamen was saying. Geraldine called
to Juanita and asked her to turn the hi-fi down, please, just a
little bit. Juanita came to the doorway, putting on her most
naïve Brigitte look. "Down with Buddy?" she asked.
"Please."
"Hm?"
"I said please but you can't hear me on account your hi-fi is so
loud."
"Hm?"
Geraldine marched up close to Juanita and said, "Mr. Kalzamen can't hear himself think and I can't even hear what he's
saying." And she gave Juanita a conspirator's confiding look that
so encouraged Juanita she turned the hi-fi down; she gave a little
encouraging wave of her fingers and even went so far as to
close the doors behind her.
Geraldine sighed and turned back to Mr. Kalzamen. "Some-

times I feel I live with Buddy Greco," she said.

"Awful to live with a man you've never even met."

Geraldine was carrying out the platter. "You carve beautifully," she said.

"You cook beautifully," he said, and his eyes followed her, filled with admiration.

"I don't thaw so beautifully, though." She shook her head at the goose, still dubious.

"No, you don't."

"I meant—" she stopped lamely, "the goose." And then realized how square she was making herself, to the extent she didn't even appreciate Mr. Kalzamen's little *double-entendres*.

Charlotte hummed along with Buddy's song, still wasping in from Juanita's side, and then said, "Something's got to give is right, Mother."

"Hm?"

"I can't reconstruct the map of Europe on the same floor as Howsmer's reconstructing the Civil War."

"The Civil War," said Howsmer.

"Hows," said Geraldine, bending down to examine the hundreds of tiny, intricately made soldiers. "Why don't you build your battlefield in the bedroom?"

"In the bedroom?" he asked, looking at her with his wide eyes. His trust in her seemed so thorough, mirrored in those luscious brown eyes, that she was almost afraid to breathe for fear of contaminating it.

"Then you won't have to worry about taking it up," she said. "You can have a permanent battlefield."

"In the bedroom?" he said again.

"Yes, darling."

Mr. Kalzamen was down on his knees, sorting out soldiers, too. "Here, Hows," he said briskly. "Let me help you. Takes men to map out strategy in wartime." And Howsmer, finding so unexpectedly an ally, began trotting back and forth to the bedroom with his own private Civil War. At one point, picking up soldiers, Mr. Kalzamen stopped and looked up at Geraldine and grinned at her. He seemed very happy. It made something catch at her throat and she accused herself of being sentimental and then forgave herself because these were her children and it was Christmas.

"You brought them such—thoughtful gifts," she said shyly.

"I think a lot of them," he said easily.

"I guess you do," said Geraldine, almost to herself, but Charlotte was listening, as Mr. Kalzamen left to finish in the bedroom with Howsmer. Geraldine looked at Charlotte and felt she must explain the little tears that were almost ready to fall. "My," she said, "Mr. Kalzamen——" But Charlotte interrupted: "He asked you to call him Kelsey."

"Kelsey—" said Geraldine exploratively.

"Yes?" said Charlotte, hopefully.

"He's a very nice man, isn't he?"

"He's nice," said Charlotte, authoritatively. "He's also intelligent and observing and attractive."

"Oh," said Geraldine, arching her neck, "is he?"

"Yes, Mother, he is." Charlotte looked at her mother a bit severely, then smiled.

"Then why don't *you* marry him?"

Charlotte sighed and looked down at her puzzle and immediately Geraldine felt contrite. "I'm sorry, Char." Charlotte smiled at her again, but Geraldine felt she was being forgiven rather than understood. Just because her daughter was precocious, Geraldine told herself, she must not forget she was a child. Mr. Kalzamen came back into the living room and helped her put the table away and then he stood with his hands on his hips, that wonderful way men have of doing, and looked at her with a grin. "Now you can't find anything to do that won't wait until later," he said. "I'll get the coffee." Geraldine laughed at him and wished that she could get the coffee instead. "If you'll sit down," he added, going out to the kitchen, so she sat down although it was just what she didn't want to do because she was afraid to. I'm only a bird in my gilded cage, she hummed to herself, and I'm afraid to settle on my little gold perch. He came back in with the coffee and cups all neatly set out on her only tray and he said, "Now, put your feet up and enjoy your day off. This isn't Howard Johnson and for me you don't have to be hostess."

"All right, Mr. K."

"You can't," he said, smiling at her sadly, "call me Kelsey, can you?"

"Sure I can. I just—forgot."

"Try to remember," he said gently. He was a gentle man and he was a gentleman and it was hard to find his flaws. Why did she think she must look for them? Only to forgive herself? For not being a worshiper of sheer virtue? Ah, ah, was it this then that troubled the world?

Charlotte watched the shadows passing across her mother's face and she said comfortingly to Mr. Kalzamen, "Just be a little patient with her, Kelsey. She's not very good at remembering." And then they all laughed together.

"What time is it?" said Geraldine.

"Eight-thirty."

"Two more hours. . . ."

"Why couldn't you take off the whole of Christmas Day," he asked; "be with your children?"

"Got to earn a living," she said. "Besides, double time for Christmas Day. At least I had to put in half a day at that rate of pay."

"I could easily afford——"

"But I couldn't."

He settled back against the sofa, watching her with his soft spaniel adoring eyes. "I got to hand it to you. Fortitude, pride, honor, independence——"

"Whoa," she said, laughing. She had to laugh to keep from blushing. "I think it's all just stubbornness, Mr. Kal—Kelsey."

"No," he said, quite firmly. He took her hand and he kissed it. "You've got strength and determination, like a pioneer woman—I admire that. Don't be uneasy. Charlotte knows I admire you, don't you, Charlotte?"

Without looking up, Charlotte said, "Yup," and her mother suddenly wondered how much it was costing Charlotte to be always the diplomat. She wanted to reach out to her, but Charlotte . . . she suddenly realized (was tonight her time for sudden knowledge of her own children?) that Charlotte was not easy to reach out to.

"And that my intentions are honorable," Mr. Kalzamen added.

"Kelsey——" said Geraldine quickly.

"You don't have to answer to that," he said. "Not now. The fact is, you're an unusual woman. That's the fact. We don't have to dispute it. You don't know. I do. I know." He looked at the ceiling. "There's something about you that *deserves*——" and he stopped a moment, looking at her. "You deserve love," he said. "I'm not good enough for you."

Juanita burst through her French doors just as Geraldine was about to protest, followed by the waves of Buddy Greco's song, and exuding such a heady locomotion of glamor and excitement that there was nothing to do but pay heed. "You don't mind," she began, "if I use your full length, do you, Gerry darling?" She batted her beaded eyelashes at Mr. Kalzamen. "Not that I ain't got one of my own, Mr. Calcimine; what's a girl these days without a full length of her own, but the light's not right in my jernt as it is in fronta Gerry's, if you know what I mean?"

Mr. Kalzamen grunted some understanding of what she meant.

"Besides," said Geraldine drily, and partly to protect Mr. Kalzamen, "if the truth were known, you want to show off your sexy dress."

"So there's nothing secretive about that!" Juanita shook her hands above her head and the shakes went on down her body until they settled in her hips; she did a shimmy twist in front of Geraldine's floor-length mirror, the layers of white fringe on her dress shimmering and shaking in the multicolored reflections of the Christmas tree. Juanita laughed pleasantly at herself. She was the sprited spirit of Christmas present, thought Geraldine, feeling a little herself like the spirit of Christmas past.

"Nice, eh?" Juanita asked, and she shook her hips again. "Eh, Mr. Calcimine?" She shook it all again. "My new twist dress." She threw back her head and laughed with childish glee. "Hm-mm."

Juanita looked pensively at Mr. Kalzamen for a moment. "Can you imagine, Mrs. Geraldine, me he can look at with my figger and this dress and all he takes is a passing glance, so much he's only got eyes for you." She turned back to examine herself in the mirror. "I used to think all a girl needed was a heavenly figger, but, boy, was I wrong. A heavenly figger, sure, and you got the eyes of the wolves, but a decent man is looking elsewhere. Although I ain't sure for what. You sure, Gerry, that my hair oughtn't go more blond? No? Don't I remind you of Audrey Hepburn, Mr. Calcimine? I mean a blondish Audrey Hepburn. You seen "Breakfast at Tiffany's"—remember it? The storya my life. Literal. They musta sat right beside my bed the week they made that one. I'm a looker, I know it, and I'm a kook, just like she was, and men, what are men to me, here today and gone tomorrow and who can even remember their names, I ask? But heartbreak? To look at me would ya think I'd ever had heartbreak in my life, no, you would not. But ask me, have I? Have I? Leave me tell you, it's bad as Audrey's. I had a brother, too, you din't know that, did you, Mrs. Geraldine? Well, he's dead now, but he's the only man I ever really respected. But the rest! The rest of it! I mean, at sixteen I got nothin', see, but nothin'. A lousy mother who don't give a mealy damn and all that, the usual story, you know. But I got this figger so what the hell there's always a place in the world for a girl with a figger, so I get myself in the line at the Radio City Music Hall. Four years I danced there and believe you me, kid, that there is no picnic. Sure, men you get to know, and all crumbs." And with that, Juanita departed into her own side of the house.

Mr. Kalzamen seemed a little stunned. "You're very patient," said Geraldine, conspiratorily.

"Sure," he grinned. "I'm filled with virtues. She sees 'em, even if you don't."

"You know I do."

"Just virtues aren't enough," said Mr. Kalzamen. "So I'm listening to her life story instead of yours."

Juanita came back in with long glass earrings that twisted along with the dress in perfect harmony. "I love crystal," she said. "I think that's because I think crystal. Ever know a girl who thought crystal before, Mr. Calcimine? Like a chandelier, I am. Teardrops of crystal, that's me. So I met a man, of course. A girl like me always would. So what if he was a Puerto Rican, Geraldine?" She turned and looked at Geraldine with defiance.

"Sounds fine," said Geraldine, still bewildered by this new

concept Juanita had of her.

"Oh, I know what you're thinking," Juanita said wisely. She turned to Mr. Kalzamen with one of her sardonic Susan Hayward looks. "She's against Spics, against Spivs, against Jews—" and then she caught her hand prettily up to her mouth—"oh, I beg your pardon, Mr. Calcimine." She went bravely on. "My mother, slob though she was, she woulda died if she'd known I went and married a Puerto Rican. Her little girl, hitched to a PR! But he was very handsome, you know, how them Latins can be when they're really beautiful? I mean, eyelashes you could use for ski slopes when it's winter, out to here! Whoever that Rudolpho Valentino was, he had nothin' on the boy I married. A real beauty he was. Not that a girl should marry for beauty, you understand, because after all beauty is only skin deep, but we were sure one marvey lookin' couple. I was even blonder then." She touched her hair in the mirror. "Are you sure, Geraldine?"

"I'm not sure."

"But talk about luck," Juanita said to Mr. Kalzamen. "His father's got money. Can you imagine? Me, marrying for beauty, and turns out his old man's got dough. Half of Puerto Rico he owns. So not much time hasa pass before I catch my pretty little hubby right in the act, and I slaps on him the habeaus corpus so fast it would make your head ring, and I got myself a cara my own and a garagea my own and housea my own and flush him down the drain there's plenty more where he came from." She turned to Howsmer and saw he wasn't there, so she directed herself to Charlotte, making her into a plural. "Okay, my kiddies, shake a leg. Auntie Juanita's ready on the town."

"You don't have to take them," said Geraldine.

"Of course not," said Juanita. "I wanta. Charlotte Russe? My God, how could any kid ever get so engrossed over a jiggle puzzle of the mapa Europe?"

Geraldine stood at the bedroom door, looking at her son, who was fast asleep among the scattered ruins of an entire army of lead soldiers.

"So wake him," said Juanita.

"He's watched that train go round so many times, it's mesmorized him."

"So unmeserve him."

"Poor little tyke," said Mr. Kalzamen. "The war was too much for him, too."

"He's always sleepin' on the floor," said Juanita. "My God, I never saw so many damn soldiers in all my life!" She shook her head, in awe. "So wake him."

Mr. Kalzamen shook his head right back at her. "I think Howie's ready for the night, Juanita." And he picked Howsmer up gently in his arms and carried him over to the bed, placing him down as if he were angel's feathers.

"Okay," said Juanita. "Me and Charlotte Russe is a team. Come on, ducks." She helped Charlotte into her coat. "Take your eyes offa that puzzle and watch where you're goin' with the arms." She took Charlotte Russe by the hand and called out to the bedroom, "So long, you two. Don't do anything I wouldn't do," and as they walked out to the car, she muttered to Charlotte, "I hope the hell they do, Charlotte Russe. If you know what I mean."

"I know what you mean, Juanita."

"That's the trouble," said Juanita, and away they drove.

Geraldine watched Mr. Kalzamen with Howsmer, taking off the shoes, putting on the pajamas, and snuggling the boy under the covers. "You do that like a father," she said.

"I should have been."

"You never——"

"My wife couldn't."

"You should have adopted——"

"To my wife, it was a disgrace she never got over." He sighed, shaking his head. "Maybe that's what she died of, the disgrace."

He sat looking for a moment at the sleeping Howsmer and then he grinned at Geraldine and got up and walked past her into the kitchen. "What are you doing now?" she asked him.

"You can't let anyone do anything for you?"

Geraldine lifted her shoulders, as if to say it was an unaccustomed role and so perhaps she wasn't playing it so well. She began to think how many, many years it had been since anyone had done the little things for her, and her thoughts skipped over her college roommate and all the way back to her father. She looked at Mr. Kalzamen and she thought of her father; her father is the one person who might have understood why Mr. Kalzamen was such an estimable and admirable man and yet still. No one else could grant her the yet still.

He heated the coffee and told her to go back to the living room and sit down. "You look," he said, "like a bird about to fly." And as she walked around her living room, Geraldine felt she was indeed what she looked like and that her living room was a cage and in a minute Mr. Kalzamen would enter the cage with her. She took up a cigarette, struck a match, then blew the match out and put the cigarette down without lighting it. She paced up and down the cage for a minute, but when she found herself counting the number of steps from the Christmas tree to the sofa and from the sofa to the door, she picked up the cigarette and lit it, sat herself down on the sofa and practiced relaxation. Mr. Kalzamen came back with the coffee tray.

"You make good coffee," he said.

"A Howard Johnson hostess should make good coffee."

"I'll bet the others don't."

"I must ask them."

"Why are you so nervous?"

He asked it very gently, without looking at her and so without forcing her, so she watched him put sugar in his coffee and thought that even his fingernails looked strong and solid.

"I'm—I'm afraid," she confessed.

"Of me?"

His shirt was white as swan's down and the broadcloth so fine it almost glistened; is there anything, she thought, more handsome than a good man's white shirt, and then corrected herself, ironically, to mean a man's good white shirt. Both applied to Mr. Kalzamen. All those words like 'good' applied. And even beyond that, there were those solid, strong shoulders which filled out that white shirt so well. If only . . .

"Of what you're going to say," she said quickly.

"I'm going to say I love you and I want you to marry me." He was still kind; he still didn't look at her or force her.

Geraldine let out her breath as if the room were frosty.

"So is that to be afraid of?" he said, and she wanted to say, Oh, yes, it is, it is more than anything else. If only the marriage part were not there, then . . . But he said then, "Geraldine, look at me," and so she did. Then he looked quickly away, saying, "No, better you not look at me. You only send me to pieces when you look." She felt a thrill of power and then a stab of envy; if only she would be sent to pieces when someone looked at her; and if only that someone were Mr. Kalzamen how cozy all the world could be. He got up and stood in front of the tree. "What I can't understand is," he said, "how a girl like you is still left single?"

I can't understand it, either, she said; surely there must be someone in the world if she just looked long enough. "Two years you've been divorced," he said, "and no one has grabbed you." Only to pinch; and never to be grabbed back. "And seven years since you've seen that husband," Mr. Kalzamen shook his head at the ways of bad men. "He was a rat. Deserting a girl like you, with two little kids——"

"No argument," said Geraldine. "He was a rat fink." Well, probably he was; everyone else seemed to think so and almost everyone always had; but, still, the sight of him was enough to turn any girl's head and the caress of him enough to keep you in bondage long past sensibility. He was gone, though, even if he were to come back, he was gone for her, and she no longer felt those pangs at night at the thought of him. "Maligning him won't solve our problem, Mr. Ka—Kelsey," she said, and it was nice to hear those rational words coming from her. At first, it was nice; then she thought, it's all going to be rational and that's the trouble. But even that wasn't true; there was something so physical about this man; you couldn't just knock that off with words like "rational."

"I donno," said Mr. Kalzamen, grinning at her. "Maybe I'm a rat fink, too."

And she laughed back at him, shaking her head at such a concept. "Oh, no. No, no."

"You can only fall in love with rat finks? A good man you can't take?"

"I'm not that experienced at rat finks, Mr. Kalzamen." He

looked apologetic. He looked even more appealing when he
looked apologetic. He had such a nice face; plain, true, plain,
but nice. What's nice to do with love? "Who knows, when you
fall in love?" she said, opening her arms to show the unknow-
ingness of the ways of the world. "Love is what you fall into,
Mr.——— Kelsey. What they turn out to be, you find out after.
Maybe my husband wasn't a rat fink when I married him; I like
to think he only got that way later. And I probably was part
responsible."

"Well," said Mr. Kalzamen, "he sure got that way."

"Yes, he sure did. And I'm sure you wouldn't."

"Then why?" He was pacing up and down now, trying to figure it out, but more than that, trying to show her that it only
made sense his way. "Why? You got two kids and this little
cheesebox of a house and that crazy nympho next door who's
not good for having around little kids growing up." He looked
very sternly toward Juanita's side of the house. She felt suddenly
that she must bristle and defend Juanita; Juanita was a part of
life, too, and she didn't want her kids growing up thinking it
was all straight and narrow. Still, Juanita was too much, she
supposed; but damn it, she liked Juanita. "You need me, Geraldine," he said. She could only nod, dumbly. "I'm so repulsive?"

"It's not that," she said. "You know that." And then she looked
at him with a smile. "Charlotte's right. You're attractive. She says
you are and you are." He looked pleased. You play handball
Mondays, Wednesdays and Fridays, she thought and it made her
grin, and you do push-ups every morning and you swim four
times a week and in summer you play tennis every morning it's
not raining and your waistline is the same as when you were in
law school and your body's hard as a punching bag and that
appeals to me, oh, I admit that, your body is just what any woman would want and no one could ask for more. Not just to lean
against because I get tired of being a woman and trying to cope;
oh, no, not just that, oh, no. She liked to think of going to bed
with him; she found she had to put that out of her mind, but
when he looked at her strong and stern like that, it wasn't easy
to ignore.

"Some days," she said, "it's all too much for me. Howard Johnson's and standing on my feet. When I was a waitress it wasn't so bad, flat shoes; but a hostess must wear the spike heels, look classy and sexy, you know. I think I'm getting too old for spike heels all day. Or all night. In two years I'll be thirty-one and I don't want to be too old. I want to worry about fixing up my hair, not worry about where is the money coming from to fix Howsmer's teeth. I know, I know," she said quickly to keep him from saying what she knew he would say, "I could move right into your nine-room apartment and look out over Central Park and just ride up and down on the elevator and not worry about a thing."

He nodded. "I got a woman comes in every day to clean but there's nothing dirty." He looked at Geraldine as if love would burst out all over him. "Bring the kids and come dirty up my place, will you, Geraldine?" And then he came over to sit next to her and he kissed her. She almost groaned with the pleasure of it, but when he put his arms around her, she fluttered her hands in the air and she tried to think of all the reasonable things she could so that she could push him gently away.

"You responded," he said, not hurt so much as insistent on the truth. "I felt you respond. Why pull away? I'm not so repulsive to you then?"

"I keep telling you," she laughed, "just because your hair's thin doesn't matter."

"I'm forty-one years old," he said, "which is just the right age for a woman like you, and I've got a good business, so maybe it's Seventh Avenue and not the law but it's respectable and I can take time off now when we need it. I take good care of myself and——"

"And your waistline's the same as when you were in law school," she teased.

"So I'm monotonous," he grinned at her.

"No." She said it matter of factly. "I just admire that fact so much. It astounds me. My waistline's not the same, I can tell you that!"

"Even when you make fun of me," he said, "I like it. I enjoy you. I love you."

Oh, dear, she thought to herself, and to keep herself from

anything else she kept talking. "I'm saying to you, Mr. Kalzamen, Kelsey dear, I'm saying: have a little confidence in yourself. The trouble is, I do find you attractive. I have to put up these struggles *not* to crawl into bed with you. For a girl like me, as Juanita points out, that's not easy." She rolled her eyes in mock dismay. "You live with Juanita a while, you start to sound like her!" She laughed. "I mean, I'm a good, healthy, red-blooded American female and you're an attractive man and there aren't many of them around these days and I should count my blessings I even met you. I don't know, Kelsey; American men have turned into crumbs." He looked very pleased to know that. "And," she said, "and it's been a long time since my genes and chromosomes have responded so—so vividly—so stay over there, Kelsey Kalzamen, because if I give in to you, we're lost and it won't be fair, it won't be fair to you and it won't be fair to me and it won't be fair to anyone." She thought she might start to cry so she stopped talking. He took her by the shoulders and shook her. "So what is fair?" he asked her. "What is fair, tell me, Geraldine?"

"Love is fair," she said, nearly in tears. "Love is fair, that's what. Love's the only thing that's fair."

"But I love you!" And he kissed her and he held her and he kissed her again.

"But," she struggled to get her breath, "I don't love you, Mr. Kelsey, I mean Mr. Kalzamen."

"You will."

She shook her head and moved to the end of the sofa. "Love isn't something you learn," she said. "Love's something that happens. I deserve love, Mr. K. If I don't get anything else out of life, and maybe I don't deserve anything else, I deserve love." He moved over to kiss her on the neck and she pretended he hadn't. "Just because I've got a sense of humor, does that mean I don't deserve love? Sometimes I think—" he kissed her again and she sat up very straight—"that only squares get love."

"I don't care," he said, close to her ear, "if you do think I'm a square."

"Well, you are, a little, I suppose. . . ."

"Then marry me."

"That's a nonsequitur, Kelsey."

He was so close to her she had to lean against the arm of the sofa and then he was on top of her and all she could think was I mustn't let him do this, I mustn't, but she couldn't think of a way to stop him, not a single way. He unbuttoned the top of her dress and covered her shoulders with kisses and then she felt the good roughness of his beard on her breast and she thought she might cry but she made herself talk instead.

"If I go to bed with you, Mr. Kalzamen, it will just be sex. It'll just be because you're an attractive man with a manly body and a way of making love that I can't resist because I need to be made love to, but it won't be love, Mr. Kalzamen, it won't be love!"

"Then marry me," he said roughly, and his hands were everywhere she thought.

"And if I marry you," she said the words aloud and tried to enunciate them very clearly although she felt the fog was setting in, "it'll just be to make things safe and easy for me and the kids, so I can get my hair done and lose weight and get some clothes that fit right and sleep late in the morning, yes I'll be indolent and sleep late in the morning. And to give my son a father because with me trying to be both father and mother to him he never says a sentence of his own but just echoes whatever his damned genius of a sister says or what I say or what that Juanita says and it's bad enough hearing what Juanita says least of all saying it, too. A boy shouldn't grow up in a houseful of women, especially when one of them has an IQ of 398 and one of them is a loose lady running around in her bare ass all day and the other one's his mother who's away at work all the time. . . ." She was crying now and she hated it; this was absolutely no time to cry because crying only meant you felt sorry for yourself and what right did she have to feel sorry for herself. "Don't," she said, "oh, please, Mr. Kalzamen, don't."

"You have a beautiful body," his muffled voice came from somewhere in that fog.

"I want a beautiful soul," she said. "I have a beautiful body," she chanted. "I have a beautiful body." She put her teeth together because they were chattering. "I have a beautiful body. What a dumb thing to say. You leave it alone. I didn't give it to you. Oh, why am I crying? I hate ladies that cry. I don't love you,

dear Mr. Kalzamen. I tried but I can't. I admire you and you are
a fine man and you would be an ideal father for my children and
a good husband to me, if I deserved a good husband, but admiration isn't love, Mr. Kalzamen." And then she called out, so
desperately, "Oh, sweet Jesus, what's the good of kids if they
don't interrupt when they shouldn't? Charlotte!!" Her voice rang
out over the rooftops and through the snow. "Charlotte! Charlotte Russe."

"Don't call Howsmer," said Mr. Kalzamen; she could hear his
voice against her stomach.

"And that good-for-nothing next door, where is she now, at a
time like this, when you really want her barging in, does she
barge? Oh, no, she's discreet and takes your very own daughter
out for a walk. Oh, stop, stop, stop, darling Mr. Kalzamen,
stop——" And she let out a sob and the tears rolled down her
face. "You have the sweetest lips," she said, "and such gentle
hands, much too tender for me, much too tender for what I deserve. All I deserve is love, not goodness, but is that asking too
much? It can't be too much to ask, it's not such a lot, is it? Just
everything." Oh, she cried and cried and wished the tears would
stop and knew in a minute they would and then . . . "Oh, I do,
I do deserve love, not just to give in because I can't fight back
any more——" It was cruel and she tried to make him hear it
but he didn't care. "Oh, this isn't the way things are supposed
to be. Kelsey, Kelsey, it isn't fair." But then, at last, she was quiet
and with a soft sigh, she smiled.

JOHN HOLLANDER
Two Poems

Helicon

Allen said, *I am searching for the true cadence.* Gray
Stony light had flashed over Morningside Drive since noon,
Mixing high in the east with a gray smoky darkness,
Blackened steel trusses of Hell-Gate faintly etched into it,
Gray visionary gleam, revealing the clarity of
Harlem's grid, like a glimpse of a future city below:
When the fat of the land shall have fallen into the dripping pan,
The grill will still be stuck with brown crusts, clinging to
Its bars, and neither in the fire nor out of it.
So is it coming about. But in my unguessing days
Allen said, *They still give you five dollars a pint at St. Luke's,
No kickback to the interne, either;* and I leaned out
Over the parapet and dug my heel in the hard,
Unyielding concrete below, and kicked again, and missed
The feeling of turf with water oozing its way to the top,
Or of hard sand, making way for life. And was afraid,
Not for the opening of vessels designed to keep
Their rich dark cargo from the air, but for the kind

JOHN HOLLANDER's most recent book of poems is entitled *Movie-going*.

Of life that led from this oldest of initiations
Ending in homelessness, despondency and madness,
And for the moment itself when I should enter through
Those dirty-gray stone portals into the hospital
Named for the Greek doctor, abandoning all hope
Of home or of self-help. The heights of Morningside
Sloped down, to the north, under the iron line
The subway holds to above it, refusing to descend
Under the crashing street. St. John the Divine's gray bulk
Posed, in its parody of history, just in the south.
Dry in the mouth and tired after a night of love
I followed my wild-eyed guide into the darkening door.

Inquiries and directions. Many dim rooms, and the shades
Of patient ghosts in the wards, caught in the privileged
Glimpses that the hurrying visitor always gets;
Turnings; errors, wanderings; while Allen chattered on:
I mean someday to cry out against the cities, but first
I must find the true cadence. We finally emerged
Into a dismal chamber, bare and dusty, where, suddenly
Sunlight broke over a brown prospect of whirling clouds
And deepening smoke to plummet down, down to the depths
Of the darknesses, where, recessed in a tiny glory of light,
A barely-visible man made his way in a boat
Along an amber chasm closing in smoke above him—
Huge paintings by Thomas Cole hung there for us to read
In the wonder of being lost, next door to the blood bank.

We waited then and the dead hospital-white of the cots
Blinded my eyes for a while, and filled my ears with the silence
Of blanketing rushes of blood. Papers and signatures. Waiting;
And then being led by the hand into a corner across
The narrow room from Allen. We both lay down in the
    whiteness.
The needle struck. There was no pain, and as Allen waved,
I turned to the bubbling fountain, welling down redly beside me
And vanishing into the plasma bottle. My life drained of richness
As the light outside seemed to darken.

                              Darker and milder the stream
Of blood was than the flashing, foaming spray I remembered
Just then, when, the summer before, with some simple souls who
        knew
Not Allen, I'd helped to fill Columbia's public fountains
With some powdered detergent and concentrated essence of
        grape,
Having discovered the circulation of water between them
To be a closed system. The sun of an August morning fired
Resplendently overhead; maiden teachers of English
From schools in the south were moving whitely from class to class
When the new, bubbling wine burst from the fountain's summits
Cascading down to the basins. The air was full of grapes
And little birds from afar clustered about their rims,
Not daring to drink, finally, and all was light and wine.
I forgot what we'd felt or said. My trickle of blood had died,
As the light outside seemed to brighten.
                              Then rest; then five dollars. Then Allen
Urged us out onto the street. The wind sang around the corner,
Blowing in from the sound, and a siren screeched away
Up Amsterdam Avenue. *Now you have a chocolate malted
And then you're fine,* he said, and the wind blew his hair like
        feathers,
And we both dissolved into nineteen forty-eight, to be whirled
Away into the wildwood of time, I to leave the city
For the disorganized plain, spectre of the long drink
Taken of me that afternoon. *Turning a guy
On,* said Allen last year to the hip psychiatrists
Down in Atlantic City, *that's the most intimate thing
You can ever do to him.* Perhaps. I have bled since
To many cadences, if not to the constant tune
Of the heart's yielding, and now I know how hard it is
To turn the drops that leaky faucets make in unquiet
Nights, the discrete tugs of love in its final scene
Into a stream, whether thicker or thinner than blood, and I
        know
That opening up at all is harder than meeting a measure:
With night coming on like a death, a ruby of blood is a treasure.

West End Blues

The neon glow escapes from
Inside; on a cracked red leather booth poets
  Are bursting into laughter,
    Half in death with easeful love. They feign
Mournful ballads made to their mistresses' highbrow

    "Lalage, I have lain with thee these many nights"
      But I hadn't, really,
      Only once, and when
    We got into the room I'd borrowed from a logician
    We left the lights off (so that when the sun broke through
      Her sleep in the morning
She screamed at the sudden gray sight of the newspaper picture
    of Henry
Wallace, tacked up on the wall, looking as if he had bad breath)

You bastards! my girl's in there,
  Queening it up in the half-light

    O salacious tavern!
    Bob taught me the chords of "Milenberg Joys" there
      But there was nothing of the
      Shadows of evening
      Red sunsets across railroad tracks in them, no train
        whistles:
      They were disappointing

    They've taken out the bar that lay along the wall
      And put one in the middle
      Like a bar in Indiana
    (Not the Regulator where there were hardboiled eggs)

"Approchez-vous, Néron, et prenez votre place,"
Said Donald, and there I was, skulking like Barrault

44

After his big dance in *Les Enfants du Paradis*
When Lemaître takes him out for coffee: "Yes, Ma," I said
While the frightfully obscure breed of terrier waddled
From lap to lap, ignoring his dish of sorrowful beer,
And later on in the evening, swimming through the smoke,
Visions of others came upon us as we sat there,
Wondering who we were: One, who followed a dark
Form down along the steps to the water of the river,
Always seemed to have just left for his terrible moment;
Someone in Galveston, setting out for Dakar,
Was never far away. As a bouncy avatar
Of "Bye Bye Blackbird" flew out of its flaming cage
Of juke-box colored lights yet once more, finally
I would arise in my black raincoat and lurch my way
Out to the street with a shudder. The cold and steamy air
Carrying protein smells from somewhere across the river,
Clustered about me, bearing me out of Tonight, into
A late hour like any other: as when at five in the morning,
Clatter of milk cans below his window on the street
Alternating with hushed unstressed sounds of long hair
And pillowslips beside his window on the bed,
Suddenly the exhausted undergraduate sees his prize
Poem taking its shape in a horribly classical meter,
So would the dark of common night well up around me
As the revolving door emptied me onto the street.

Salax taberna!
          And you, boys, in there, past the third
          Corner away from Athena's corny little owl
          (Hiding for shame inside those public and politic skirts)
              Are you all that's well-hung around here?
              Laddies lined up at the bar,
              Is it no one else can be game
              For everything? I'll take you on
              There's nothing and no one I won't do.
You bastards, my girl's in there,
    Queening it up in the half-light

45

Across Broadway and down a bit, the violent
Fluorescence and fierce tile of Bickford's always shone
Omnisciently, and someone sad and crazy said,
"God lives in Bickford's"
                    But that was after they started
            Serving sandwiches inside the bar
            Thinner than the coffee cups,
            When we had all become spectres too,

And eyes, younger eyes, would glisten all unrecognizing
As heads turned, interrupting the stories
        They were innocently and inaccurately
Telling about us, to watch the
        Revolving door make a tired,
Complete turn, as the shape
        Huddled inside it hardly
Bothered to decide
        Not to go in at all,
Having been steered there only by the heart's mistakes,
An unbroken habit in the treasonable night.

JEAN PAULHAN

The Marquis de Sade & His Accomplice
or, The Revenges of Modesty

THE SECRET OF *Justine*

We have known for some time why the New Testament is the world's greatest best seller. It is because this book has a secret. Because on every page, in every line, it hints at something which it does not reveal, but which tempts us, arrests us, fascinates us all the more. And since we shall here be concerned with the Gospels no further, what is to prevent us from betraying this secret?

The secret is that Jesus is joyous. The New Testament shows him to us as solemn and rather pensive, sometimes irritable, sometimes in tears, always very serious. But we can suppose something the New Testament does not tell us: that every now and then Jesus made a joke, that he had a sense of humor, that sometimes he spoke without rhyme or reason, just to see what

JEAN PAULHAN, editor of *La Nouvelle Revue Française* for forty of his seventy years, has recently been made a member of the French Academy. The author of many books, he is best known for his studies of Braque, cubism and Dubuffet, his translations from the Malagasy, and his heroism in the French Resistance. His most recent work is the long preface to *Histoire d'O*.

would happen (as when he addressed the fig trees). In short, that he amused himself.

I do not wish to offend anyone by comparing these Gospels with the most ingenious as well as the bulkiest Gospel of Evil ever written, with full consciousness and rationality, by a man in total revolt. Nevertheless, if *Justine* deserves its place as the bedside book—for a certain period of their lives, at least—of Lamartine, Baudelaire and Swinburne, Barbey d'Aurévilly and Lautréamont, Nietzsche, Dostoevsky and Kafka (and on a slightly different level, of Sacher-Masoch, Ewers, and Mirbeau), it is because this strange, apparently simple book, which nine-teenth-century writers have taken such pains—though scarcely once referring to it by name—to apply, to refute, to plagiarize, this book which asked so serious a question that it was not too much work for a whole century to answer it (and, at that, not in full), this book too has a secret. I shall return to it. But let us settle the moral question first.

I. CONCERNING CERTAIN DANGEROUS BOOKS

Everything has supposedly been said about the benefits of punishment and the advantages of legal chastisement. There are a thousand opinions on the subject in circulation, and a hundred thousand books. And yet it seems to me that the point has been missed: perhaps because it appeared too obvious, because it went without saying. In which case it will go still better *with* saying.

One point is all too obvious: criminals are dangerous; they imperil society and the human race itself. From this point of view, for instance, it would be better if there were no murderers. If the law left each of us free to kill his neighbors (as we often wish to do) and his parents (as the psychoanalysts claim we secretly desire), not many people would remain on the face of the earth. Only our friends. And not even our friends, since after all—although this is a detail generally ignored—even our friends are *somebody's* fathers, sons, or neighbors. I pass on to the second point, which is no less obvious, when you come to think about it.

It is that criminals are generally more interesting than honest people: less predictable, providing more food for thought. And even when they say (as it turns out) only banal things, criminals are more surprising: precisely because of this contrast they offer between the dangerous depths and the inoffensive surface. It is a matter of common knowledge among detective-story writers: as soon as we suspect the gallant notary or the pharmacist of having once poisoned a whole family, his most insipid statements become precious to us, and if he remarks that the weather is changing, we immediately suspect him of plotting some new crime. The moralists claim that it is enough to have taken, even accidentally, a single human life in order to feel oneself entirely transformed. And the moralists are imprudent to say so, for we all want to be transformed. It is a feeling as old as the world itself, practically the story of Eve and the apple. And if considerations of prudence generally keep us from transforming ourselves to this extent, at least we have a strong desire to frequent those who have passed through the ordeal, to make them our friends, to espouse their repentance (and the wisdom that follows from it). The only thing that holds us back, at this point, is the sentiment I mentioned earlier: a murderer is not a gentleman to be encouraged; by admiring him we participate in a great conspiracy against man and society. And if we should happen to be scrupulous, we find ourselves worried past endurance, sniped at from right and left alike, deprived of the advantages of both good and bad conscience. Here punishment intervenes.

I should go so far as to say that punishment reconciles everything. The moment the thief discovers he has been robbed—if not always of his money, at least of several years of his life, worth as much as the money or even more—and the murderer murdered, we can enjoy their company without the slightest qualm, and—for instance—while they are still alive, bring oranges to their cells. We can love them; we can even drink in their words; they are paying, they have paid. Which is what our kings and queens and our saints knew better than we, actually leading criminals to the steps of the scaffold itself, and collecting, like Saint Catherine, a few drops of their blood. (And who today does not owe something to those who teach us, in their torment, the danger and the very meaning, which we have lost, of treason?)

Which brings me to my point: it has been customary, for a hundred and fifty years, to frequent Sade by means of certain intermediary authors. We do not read *Les Crimes de l'Amour*, but, for example, *l'Auberge de l'Ange Gardien* (the Countess of Ségur); not *la Philosophie dans le Boudoir*, but *Beyond Good and Evil*; not *les Infortunes de la Vertu*, but *The Castle* or *The Trial*; not *Juliette*, but *les Diaboliques* (Barbey d'Aurévilly); not *La Nouvelle Justine*, but *le Jardin des Supplices* (Mirbeau); not *le Portefeuille d'un Homme de Lettres* (which has been lost anyway), but *les Mémoires d'Outre-Tombe* (Chateaubriand). And such timidity can scarcely be anything but the effect of the scruples I have mentioned. Of course it is true that Sade was a dangerous man: sensual, violent, occasionally a cheat, and (at least in fantasy) atrociously cruel. For he urges us to kill off not only our neighbors and our parents, but our wives as well. He would be even more delighted to see the whole human race disappear, making room for some new invention of nature's. In other respects, not very sociable—not even very social: infuriated by liberties. But after all, such scruples as these can be allayed.

For Sade has paid and paid amply, spending thirty years of his life in the various bastilles, strongholds, and dungeons of the Kingdom, then of the Republic, the Terror, the Consulate, and the Empire. "The freest mind," said Apollinaire, "the world has yet seen." In any case, the most imprisoned body. Some have said there is a single key to all his novels: cruelty (which, I think, is far too simple a view). But there is, much more certainly, a single conclusion to all his adventures and all his books: prison. There is even something mysterious about so many arrests and confinements.

Let us confront his crimes with his punishments. It seems established that Sade administered a flogging to one Parisian prostitute: did this deserve a year in the dungeons? That he gave cantharides pastilles to some girls in Marseilles: did this deserve ten years in the Bastille? That he seduced his sister-in-law Louise: did this deserve a month in the Conciergerie? That he unceasingly provoked his powerful, his formidable parents-

in-law, the Président and Présidente de Montreuil: did this deserve two years in a provincial dungeon? That he helped a few
Moderates escape (it was the height of the Terror): did this
deserve a year in Les Madelonnettes? It is admitted that he
published obscene books, that he attacked Bonaparte's entour-
age; it is not impossible that he feigned madness: did this deserve fourteen years in Charenton, three years in Bicêtre, a year
in Sainte-Pélagie? How can we avoid the conclusion that any
pretext was good enough for the various governments of France
(he had seen them all!) to throw him into prison. But setting
this aside, one point, at least, has been established: we know
that Sade ran risks; that he accepted them—even multiplied
them. We also know that in reading his books we perhaps run
our risks as well. Hence I am free to dream as much as I like
about what was good, and in any case about what was delightful
in this little nephew of the chaste Laure de Noves: about his
extreme distinction; about his blue eyes, which even as a child
attracted feminine attention; about that suspicion of languor in
his figure; about those "most beautiful teeth imaginable";[1] about
his impetuous but subtle repartee (immodest, perhaps, but never
unbuttoned); about this young Provençal nobleman whose vas-
sals come to kiss his hands and who is pursued by the all-too-
faithful love, the love-in-spite-of-everything of his big Renée,
who was a little horsey, perhaps, but sweet and courageous at
heart.

II. THE DIVINE MARQUIS

I shall not discuss the special effectiveness to which Duclos
alludes in speaking of books read with one hand only. Of course
such books are interesting—to a certain degree they are sensa-
tionally so: more than one author, even among the most abstract, has hoped his works might enjoy an analogous influence
or repercussion (on other levels, of course). The fact remains
that there is not much to say about them, their effectiveness
ordinarily being unforeseeable. Besides, it is commonly admitted

---

[1] We do not know of a single portrait of Sade. I borrow these features from
letters, police reports, and from the image of himself Sade provides in the
description of Valcour.

that concealment and allusion (badinage and licentiousness, if
you prefer) are more likely to provoke this kind of effectiveness
than obscenity pure and simple. Now there is little concealment
and less allusion in Sade. Which is perhaps what is held against
him most. Nothing could be less characteristic of Sade than the
self-satisfied smile, the naughty implication we find in Bran-
tôme's French-fried stories, the lewd passages in Voltaire or
Diderot, the jigsaw art Crébillon brings to such discouraging
perfection in his alcove anecdotes. There is a freemasonry of
such literary pleasures by which every initiate can interpret the
meaningful winks, the half-spoken propositions, the suspension
points. But Sade breaks with these conventions. As free from
the laws and rules of the erotic novel as Poe from those of the
detective story, or Victor Hugo from those of the *roman feuille-
ton* (serialized novel), Sade is unfailingly direct, explicit—and
tragic besides. If we must classify him at all costs, he would
more likely be found among those authors who castrate their
readers (as Montaigne puts it). Furthermore, there is yet another kind of appeal which he declines.

An appeal we might label the *literary lure*. More than one
celebrated work derives its value—or in any case its success—
from an ingenious system of allusions. Voltaire's tragedies,
Delille's poems, in every line evoke—and take credit for evok-
ing—Corneille or Racine, Virgil, Homer, and company. To consider only Sade's immediate rival (his competitor, so to speak,
in Evil, it is evident that Laclos is rotten with literature—a
corruption he manages to turn to the wickedest, most intelligent
account. *Les Liaisons Dangereuses* is a tournament of courtly
love (the whole problem is to discover whether Valmont will
show himself to be worthy of Madame de Merteuil) with Ra-
cinian heroines for its contenders (including both Phèdre and
Andromaque) in the facile society of Crébillon, Nerciat, and
Vivant-Denon (for everything concludes swiftly enough, once
the characters are in bed—everything is envisaged, at least, from
the point of view of getting them to bed). That is the key to its
mystery: *Les Liaisons Dangereuses* includes, quite discreetly, a
short course in literary history for grownups. For the most mysterious authors are generally the most literary, and their strange-

ness derives precisely from their incongruity: from this encounter of characters from the remotest possible worlds—i.e., from the remotest possible works—who are astonished to meet each other where they find themselves. Furthermore, Laclos was never able to make this superhuman effort again.

But Sade, with his gulfs and glaciers, his scary châteaux; his endless prosecution of God—and of man; his insistence, his repetitions, his appalling platitudes; his systematic mind and his perpetual ratiocinations; his stubborn pursuit of a sensational act by means of an exhaustive analysis; his continual employment of every possible part of the body (there is not one which is not made to serve), of every possible idea (Sade read as many books as Marx); his odd contempt for literary artifice, but his constant requirement of truth; his bearing of a man in constant action who at the same time is dreaming one of those indefinite dreams that instinct sometimes generates; his great expenditures of energy and even life, suggesting some terrible primitive rite—or that other kind of rite, perhaps, which we call world wars; his vast engagements with the universe, or rather the one simple engagement he was the first to bring to bear upon man (which without much of a play on words we can indeed call a bloody engagement)—with all of this, Sade has no need for selection of images and theatrical effects, elegance and amplification. He neither distinguishes nor separates. He repeats himself, perpetually assails us with the same story. He reminds us of the sacred books of the great religions. Occasionally crystallized into some maxim:

> *There are dangerous moments when man's physical nature is ignited by the errors of his morality.*
> *There is no better way to familiarize oneself with death than to combine it with some libertine idea.*
> *We inveigh against the passions without realizing that it is from their torch that philosophy lights its own . . .*

(and what maxims!) he utters that gigantic and obsessive murmur which sometimes rises out of literature (and perhaps justifies it): Amiel,[2] Montaigne, the *Kalevala*, the *Ramayana*. If some-

---

[2] It is well known that Amiel's published works are only a small part of his actual production as a writer.

one were to point out that in Sade's case, at least, it is a question
of a sacred book that has not found its religion or its congregation, I should reply first of all that it's a lucky thing it has not,
and second that we have only to congratulate ourselves on the
fact (being thereby freer to judge Sade for himself, not by his
effects). Upon reflection I would add that I am not even so sure
about this: the religion in question is by its very nature con-
demned to secrecy—reduced, for its expression, to an occasional
groan for our benefit; three lines of Baudelaire:

> *Qui recélant un fouet sous leurs longs vêtements,*
> *Mélent, dans le bois sombre et les nuits solitaires,*
> *L'écume du plaisir aux larmes des tourments.*[3]

a maxim by Joseph de Maistre:

> *Woe to the nation that suppresses torture.*[4]

a sigh from Swinburne:

> *The martyr Marquis . . .*

a moment of Chateaubriand's bravado:

> *I was always virtuous without pleasure. I would have*
> *been criminal without remorse.*

a cry from Lautréamont:

> *The delights of cruelty, delights that are not fugitive . . .*

a reflection by Pushkin:

> *. . . The joy to which we are reduced by everything that*
> *approaches death.*

Besides, I wonder about the somewhat murky pleasure taken
by Chateaubriand—and by his descendants: Barrès, Suarès,
Montherlant—in the agony of the women who have loved them,
the governments they have defended, the religions they have
believed in. There are certainly reasons—though it is difficult for
us to expose them—why Sade is now known as the divine Marquis. If we are not at all sure, on the one hand, that he was a
Marquis, it cannot be denied that a certain number of persons

---

[3] *Who, concealing a whip beneath their long garments,*
  Mingle, in the dark wood on lonely nights,
  The foam of pleasure with the tears of torture.

[4] Cf. "The submission of the populace is always a result of the violence
and the extent of the punishments with which it is met." (*La Nouvelle
Justine*, IV).

—persons, furthermore, of respectable appearance—have considered him divine, or veritably diabolic, which is on the same order.

My suspicions carry me still further. I wonder, when I see so many writers of our time so conscientiously devoted to the repudiation of artifice and literary craft in favor of some unspeakable occurrence about which we are permitted to suppose that it is both erotic and terrifying; so concerned with taking, in each circumstance, a stand contrary to Creation; so entirely given over to a quest for the sublime in the infamous, the great in the subversive; and demanding, moreover, that every work engage and compromise its author according to a kind of effectiveness not without analogies to the physiological and localized effectiveness to which I have alluded above—I wonder if we must not recognize, in a Terror as extreme as this, not so much an invention as an echo, not so much an ideal as a memorial; in short, if our whole modern literature, in just those areas where it seems to us most alive—most aggressive, in any case—is not entirely oriented toward the past, and very precisely determined by Sade, as the eighteenth-century tragedies were determined by Racine.

But I intended to speak here only of *Justine*.

III. THE SURPRISES OF LOVE

Justine, as we know, has every virtue, and discovers she is to be punished for each of them. Charitable, she is robbed by a beggar. Pious, she is raped by a monk. Honest, she is ruined by a usurer. Frank and straightforward, she is whipped and wounded by a sodomite and abandoned in the woods. She refuses to become an accomplice in a larceny, a poisoning, an armed attack (misfortune and poverty throw her among strange companions), and it is she who is held guilty of theft, highway robbery, and murder. The rest of her adventures are in keeping with this brief list. Nevertheless, to every kind of villainy Justine can only oppose a noble soul and a sensitive mind. But this would be saying little enough: she also brings good fortune to her torturers, and the monsters who abuse her become a cabinet minister, a royal surgeon, and a millionaire. This novel, in fact,

bears an extreme resemblance to those moral works in which
vice is punished at every turn and virtue instantly rewarded.
Except that in *Justine* the situation is reversed; nevertheless its
failure, from a purely literary point of view (which is our own),
remains the same: we always know how it will turn out in the
end. And this end of Sade's does not even have the banality
which ultimately makes the Triumph of Virtue into one of the
conventions of the novel as a literary form, a convention scarcely
more noticeable than its division into chapters or episodes. There
is every evidence for believing that Sade takes his lamentable
dénouements terribly seriously, and is each time genuinely
astonished by them. What is even more curious, we are astonished with him.

This astonishment poses a singular problem. Singular because
Sade declines all the facilities that are the commonplaces of his
contemporary rivals, the Gothic novelists. It is all too easy to
amaze when you invoke the assistance, as do Radcliffe or Lewis,
of phantoms, Gothic chimeras, hellish specters, and other devil-
tries in which astonishment plays a considerable part. Sade
however, wants dealings only with man; indeed, with natural
man, as he is represented, for example, by Richardson or Field-
ing.[5] Hence no ogres, no magicians, no angels, no demons—
above all, no gods!—but within man the unique faculty which
creates these gods, angels, or demons; and the vices or virtues
which by taking us unawares set this faculty in motion. The
riddle thus proposed contains only two or three words, of which
the first is quite simple, quite ordinary: modesty.

It is curious that the eighteenth century, to which we owe
the most cynical account of manners in all our literature, has
also given us our two great painters of modesty: one of these,
as everyone knows, is Marivaux. The other, whom everyone
unaccountably persists in ignoring, is Sade. It is curious, or rather
it is not curious at all. Such fear in the face of love, such defiance
of fear, such pride, such sudden withdrawals, such refusals to
see and hear, by which what subsequently came to be called
marivaudage both protects and betrays itself—for Marivaux

---

[5] Cf. *Idée sur les Romans.*

shares with Sade the dubious privilege of having given his
name to a certain form of erotic behavior; nor am I sure the
attribution is much more exact or better understood in Sade's
case than in that of Marivaux—such terror of being hurt can
only be explained or even understood if there is occasion to be
hurt, if, ultimately, love *is* dangerous. Marivaux's heroines are
as modest as if they had read *Justine*. Justine herself. . . .

Whatever happens to her, Justine is astonished. Experience
teaches her nothing. Her soul remains ignorant, her body more
ignorant still. She is scarcely allowed to lean her head to one
side here, to half-close her eyes there. She will never take the
first step. Even when she is in love, it does not occur to her to
kiss Bressac. She says: "If my imagination had sometimes
strayed among these pleasures, it was because I believed them
as chaste as the God who inspired them, given by nature to
serve as a consolation to humanity, the progeny of love and
delicacy; I was far from believing that man, after the example
of beasts. . . ."[6] Astonished each time someone gives himself
up to certain operations upon her of which she surmises the
meaning indistinctly and the interest not at all, Justine repre-
sents the most harrowing as well as—alas!—the most harrowed
image of virtue we possess. "Modesty," it was said at the time,
"is a virtue fastened on with pins. . . ." But in Justine's case the
pins are thrust into the flesh itself, which bleeds when the gar-
ment is torn away. Can it be said that the reader must have no
little good will if he is to be surprised and outraged along with
her? Not at all. First of all, the reader is free to interpret what
is described as entirely physical torment as *moral* harrowing,
as outrage to the sensibility. *Justine* is related to the fairy tales
that tell us Cinderella wears glass slippers—and we readily
understand (unless we are rather dull-witted) that it is not at
all a question of glass slippers, but of the infinite delicacy of
Cinderella's steps. Furthermore, we live unceasingly on the brink
of the strange. What is more astonishing, all things considered,
than to find at the ends of our arms these odd prehensile, reddish,
wrinkled organs called hands, and at the divergent extremities

---

[6] *Les Infortunes de la Vertu.*

of these same hands to find bits of mineral (transparent besides)! Sometimes we surprise ourselves eating, busily grinding up pieces of dead animals between those other minerals which arm our mouth. It is easy to continue, and perhaps there is not a single one of our acts that can withstand prolonged attention. Yet there exists one realm, at least, in which strangeness is neither a matter of chance nor an exception, one realm in which it is the rule.

For eating, after all, ordinarily perplexes us only slightly: we have the vague impression that our present meal is one of a succession of a thousand past meals which it strongly resembles and which serve as a kind of guarantee for the one we are eating now. But with each new love, as everyone knows, it seems—to such a degree is each feature of our beloved unique and actually inexpressible—that we have never really loved before. No matter how often the poets invoke cool springs, birds' nests, jacinths, and roses, they scarcely evoke even a hint of the astonishment life has in store for us.

It is the same astonishment that, on another level, our common speech reveals in its names for the private parts: little brother, little man, little friend, first mate, etc. What have these organs done to us, then, that we should be unable to speak of them simply? Well, this much at least: they refuse to accommodate themselves to our wishes. So that it merely remains for the novelist to bear witness to his astonishment and his perplexity.

Doubtless. Or else on each occasion to renew the reasons for this astonishment, so that it never becomes banal—tamed—for the reader, and to impose this perplexity upon him rather than merely tell him about it. This is what Sade, in his way, has done. For ultimately what do so many various treatments, so many baroque ways of seeking pleasure and making love mean, if not that love and pleasure are unceasingly astonishing and unforeseeable. As I have said, *Justine* reads, or should be read, like a fairy tale. And I add that we are concerned here only with that paradoxical—to itself almost incredible—character of love which impels the lover (as Lucretius has it) to bruise the body of his beloved.

However, the riddle has a last word.

IV. JUSTINE, OR THE NEW OEDIPUS

Sade did not wait until he was in prison to read. He had devoured the favorite works of his century. He knew the *Encyclopédie* by heart. Voltaire and Rousseau inspired him with a mixture of sympathy and horror. The horror was a matter of logic: they were incoherent; inconsistent, in the true sense of the word. But at least he accepted their principles, their requirements—their prejudices, especially the most important one of all.

The eighteenth century had just discovered—and was not a little proud of its discovery—that a mystery is not an explanation. Neither is a myth. On the contrary, no sooner do you create one myth than you must forge another to prop it up. A tortoise, say the Indians, bears the world upon its back. Very well, but what bears the tortoise? God created the world. Very well, but who created God? Of course the discovery (if we must flatter it with this name) was actually made much earlier, but it was the contributors to the *Encyclopédie* who excelled in devising its most popular and also its most fashionable form. We can now speak only historically of a God to whom Voltaire—and later Sade—opposed *man alone:* man (they said) is only man; man (Voltaire added) is not noble; man is natural man, without Mythology.

This meant, first of all, repudiating all the current charms —the facilities—of literature. It also meant exposure to a new difficulty. For after all, *man alone* had had to invent God, Spirits, satyrs, even a minotaur. And we will have made remarkably little progress in our study of this man if we have not taken into account, merely as features of human nature, not only our real societies and the passions seething within them, but the vast fantasy societies which accompany the real ones like their shadow. Such was the burden which the death of God bequeathed to literature. Voltaire is human, true enough. He is even a splendid representative of the ordinary man. Nevertheless one cannot help remembering that there have been wars and great religions, migrations and empires, the Inquisition and human sacrifices—and that men have not resembled Voltaire very often after all.

"We don't insist that they do," answers the *Encyclopédie*. "We are modest. We will have all the patience necessary. Man, at least, is our *given*: he is here, we have him before our eyes. We are companions in exile (if it is an exile that is in question). All we need do is observe him without prejudice, subject him to our investigations. He will end up by sitting down to dinner with us. If he should manage to conceal (how cunning he is!) some of his propensities, our grandchildren will eventually pluck them out of hiding. We have time on our side. For the moment, let us establish our files and complete our collections."

Sade is of his time. He too begins with analysis and patient collecting. It has long been thought that the *Cent-vingt Journées*, that gigantic catalog of perversions, formed the crowning glory of his work. Not at all: it is the foundation, the first step. A step the *Encyclopédie* itself would not have disclaimed. Sade even imposes a procedural rigor which the contributors to the *Encyclopédie* did not attempt; all of them (he thought) resorted to cheating quickly enough. Some, like Rousseau (who furthermore considered himself a special case), had petty natures and were easily reduced to sniveling, for they were ceaselessly embarrassed by each other's presence, ready to abandon man as they might have seen him, touched him, spoken to him, for the sake of any noble savage (to whom anthropology has given the lie a thousand times). Others, like Voltaire, having an insensitive, dry character, were quite incapable of believing in the truth of passions they did not experience. Others still, like Diderot, were frivolous, leaping haphazardly from one fantasy to another, incapable of maintaining any continuity in their ideas. Voltaire's man might account for the invention of the spade; Jean-Jacques' for botany; Diderot's for conversation. But ogres and inquisitions and wars? "Ah," replies Voltaire, "but these poor people were demented. We shall rectify all that." "Which is precisely what I call cheating," says Sade. "It was a question of knowing man, and already you want to change him."

It must be admitted that this rigor—which I should prefer to call this heroism—might well have misled Sade (as it misled, at about the same period, that gushing little fool who also happened to be a good writer, Restif de la Bretonne). But this was not the case. A Krafft-Ebing consecrates the categories and distinctions established by the divine Marquis, repeating them in ten volumes with a thousand examples to support his arguments. Later a Freud resumes his method and his principles as well. It is, I think, a unique example in our literature: a few novels—novels, indeed!—that have initiated, fifty years after their publication, a whole science of man. One must ultimately admit that Sade, during his periods of freedom, knew how to use his eyes even better than he had used libraries. Or else that a certain fire in his temperament caused him to experience—and to divine—the most diverse human passions. I am astonished he has not received more gratitude for his benefactions. Nevertheless it is only too evident that scientific rigor, in such matters, runs a certain risk: it generally tends to give too large and too exclusive a place to the physical aspect and expression of love (as it does to private interest in social economy). For if the existence of the soul or even the mind can easily be denied, that of coitus cannot.

Yet Sade rejects this new facility no less severely. What characterizes most erotic books, and what Sade lacks, as we have seen, is a certain superior tone (which might just as accurately be called inferior), a certain self-important manner (which might with equal justice be called unimportant); a certain degree of alienation, a certain brusque estrangement. For literature and even language hesitate over an event (sometimes called animal, or even bestial) which seems to have nothing at all to do with the mind and of which it can only be observed that it *takes place*. If the writer is Boccaccio or Crébillon, he observes this with amused satisfaction; if the writer is Marguerite de Navarre or Godard d'Aucourt, with some reservations. But it is this very otherness, this separation from the life of the mind that Sade does not accept. "Man is all of a piece and lucid," he says. "He accomplishes nothing without reason." Which accounts for the fact that his heroes accept themselves as they are, even in their aberrations, and pursue their ideas to the limit without ever losing sight of themselves. "We scoundrels," affirms one of these

heroes (and they all repeat his words at one time or another),
"pride ourselves only on our frankness and the exactitude with
which we follow our principles."[7] It is discourses and reflections
that set them going.

Which accounts for their weakness: it is also discourses and
reflections that can make them slip. For there is no argument,
however wise, which does not agree in advance to yield to a
contrary argument if it recognizes the latter as wiser still. Hence
the Lénore of *Aline et Valcour* escapes rape more than once by
the excellent pretexts she invents in the nick of time. Justine
herself discovers she is constantly invited to refute her persecu-
tors. She is never taken treacherously: "No fine feelings," says
one of her malefactors, "Reasons. I will let you go if they are
valid."[8] Now Justine has a good head on her shoulders, and the
riddles confronting her are so honestly presented—so detailed, so
explicit—that we expect her to discover the answers from one
moment to the next. Justine, or the new Oedipus.

V. THREE RIDDLES

Since Sade, most of these riddles have become world-wide pre-
occupations. The danger today is that we are tempted to deal
with them separately, whereas Sade considers them all together;
once isolated they become overfamiliar and their solution—or
the difficulty of solving them—too obvious. But let us stick to
the texts.

"First of all," says Sade, "we must be explicit. Who are you,
and what do you want in this world? Evidently there are too
many moments as it is when you sleep your life away or else
merely let yourself live, coming and going like an animated
statue. Are you this statue? No, you want to be conscious, as
conscious as possible, and rational. You desire happiness, which
multiplies consciousness and rationality. What kind of happiness? The kind usually situated in the realm of pleasure, of love.
Very well. You have only to avoid confusing the two. Loving
is essentially different from making love: as is proved by the

---

[7] *La Philosophie dans le Boudoir.*
[8] *Justine*, II.

fact that we are in love every day without making love, and that even more frequently we make love without being in love. Now if making love provides an obvious pleasure, love itself is accompanied, you will admit, by all kinds of trouble and anxiety. 'But spiritual pleasures, moral duties . . .' you will say. Of course. Can you name a single one that is not a product of the imagination? You will surely agree with me that imagination thrives on freedom; and that the joys it provides are all the keener if the imagination itself is liberated from bonds and bridles. What rules can we lay down for it in advance? Let it run free as it pleases.

"We had got as far as pleasure. Here too we must distinguish the pleasure taken from that you think you are giving. Now nature informs us quite explicitly about our own pleasure, quite inadequately about anyone else's. Can you say for sure that the woman in your arms is not feigning her pleasure? Are you so certain that when you have most 'offended' her by your erotic behavior she does not derive from her very outrage some uncertain, murky satisfaction? Let us confine ourselves to the obvious facts: delicacy, consideration, concern for our partner limit and even destroy our own pleasure, and produce uncertain results at best. Is it not therefore normal that a man should prefer what he feels to what he does not feel? And have we ever experienced a single natural impulse which led us to prefer others to ourselves?"

"Nevertheless," Justine replies, "morality . . ."

"Morality," Sade continues, "yes, let us speak of morality! Are you not aware, then, that murder is as honorable in China, as rape in New Zealand or robbery in Sparta? Why is this man being drawn and quartered in the marketplace? He has tried to perform in Paris what is a virtue in Japan. And this man, whom we leave to rot on his pallet of wet straw, what is his crime? He has read Confucius. No, Justine, these words vice and virtue, about which there is so much argument, can never give you anything but provincial notions, local ideas. At best they can teach you, if you study them well, the country in which you should have been born. Morality is geography in reverse."

"But if we were born in France . . ." Justine says.

"I was coming to that. It is quite true that here in France our ears are filled from childhood on with Charity and Kindness. It is the Christians, you know, who imagine they have invented these virtues with which more than one atheist assails us so mechanically. Do you know why? Because being slaves themselves and unprovided with this world's goods, they could gain their pleasures—and even their subsistence—only from their masters' charity. They had every interest in convincing these masters, and to that end made use of their parables, their legends, their proverbs, their whole rhetoric of persuasion. And these masters, fools that they were, let themselves be taken in! So much the worse for them. But we philosophers, better informed, seeking pleasure in our own way and with all our might, shall do what the slaves you admire did, Justine, not what they said."

"And remorse," Justine asks timidly, "what will you do about remorse?"

"Haven't you discovered that for yourself? Man only repents of what he is not in the habit of doing. Let him become accustomed to his behavior and his remorse will vanish: a single crime disquiets us, ten or twenty leave us unperturbed."

"I have never tried."

"Well, what are you waiting for? Besides, what else do we see every day in the example of the highwayman and thieves so aptly described as *hardened* criminals! Just as stupidity disposes man to faith, repeated crime renders him callous. Which is the best possible proof that virtue is only a superficial principle."

"Nevertheless," Justine insinuates, "suppose there was some original engagement between man and man, some understanding to which honor or even interest bids us remain faithful."

"Ah," Sade cries, "you raise the question of the social contract! It's quite possible. But I'm afraid you misunderstand the problem. Let us reason it out together. You claim that men, when they first organized themselves into societies, concluded this pact: I won't hurt you if you won't hurt me."

"The pact might have been a tacit one," Justine remarks. "And I don't see how, without such a pact, any society could be established or subsist."

"Very well. You mean the kind of pact we must recommence each moment, as if we were to sign it every day."

"Why not?"

"Merely observe this: that a pact of this kind presumes the equality of those who are party to it. I have renounced doing you harm: that means I was previously free to do you harm. I renounce it now: that means *I had remained free to harm you.*"

"And then?"

"Imagine, then, that you were handed over to me as a slave is handed over to his master, a prisoner to his executioner. Why would it ever occur to me to make a pact with you that would accord you certain chimerical rights and at the same time deprive me of my real rights? If you cannot harm me, why should I fear you or worry myself about you? But let us proceed further. You will agree that each of us takes pleasure in the exercise of his faculties and his particular gifts: the athlete from wrestling, the philanthropist from his good works, and the violent man from his violence. If you are entirely subject to me, it is your oppression which will give me my greatest pleasure."

"Can this be possible?" Justine asks. "Is this human?"

"I would not put my hand in the fire to swear that man is human. Yet observe this too: if the strong man takes pleasure in exercising his strength, the softhearted or weak man profits from his weakness, his compassion. He too gives himself up to pleasure. The kind of pleasure he chooses is entirely his own affair. Why the devil must I reward him for the pleasures he decides upon for himself?"

"You mean, then," Justine says, "that there are a thousand kinds of weakness and of strength?"

"Unquestionably. It is quite true that civilization, with time, has somewhat changed the natural aspect of life, yet at least it respects life's laws: the rich are today no less ferocious about exploiting the poor than the violent were in the past about harassing the weak and the wretched. All these financiers and these princes would bleed a whole people white if they thought they might find a few flakes of gold in their blood."

"It is terrible," Justine agrees, "but I must admit I have seen more than one example.

VI. THREE NEW RIDDLES

That religion, established morality and society itself are cunning inventions which permit certain men—the strongest, to be precise—to torment the rest of humanity is a notion whose validity no eighteenth-century thinker would dispute. The wise and modest Vauvenargues himself offers his arguments in the name of nature. Quite simply, Voltaire prefers to attack religion, Jean-Jacques society, and Diderot morality. And Sade all three at once. Indeed laws are harsh, repression implacable, authority despotic. We are rushing, says Sade—Sade is the only one to say it[9]—toward Revolution. Well and good. What can a man do who has grasped this truth and yet cannot free himself from so many oppressions at once?

At least he can free himself from them in his own behalf, in the secrecy of his own heart. Grimm, Diderot, Rousseau, Mademoiselle de Lespinasse, or Madame d'Epinay all abide, in questions of morality, by one article of faith which they sometimes admit, sometimes dissimulate—in every case one must discern and then pursue the first and most spontaneous of the heart's inclinations, thereby restoring within onself, by dint of patience and persistence, the primitive man, or at least his natural goodness.

Modern anthropology has torn to shreds the various accounts[10] of the noble savage that nourished so many sensitive souls around 1760. Only fairy tales are left. One might have foreseen it.

For I quite understand that the savages of Tahiti know nothing of our laws or of our moral codes. But what if they were subject to others no less severe? Or, who knows, even more cruel? (Here, ultimately, is where the early travelers' sagacity functioned. We know it was rewarded.) Let us proceed further. I see too that these savages have no carriages or canons like ours. And if it were on purpose? If they had known something like our civilization and had subsequently renounced it (as we are tempted to

---

[9] In *Aline et Valcour.*
[10] For instance, *Sauvages de Thaïti, Histoire des Sévérambes, Voyages de Bougainville, Suppléments aux Voyages,* and *Suppléments aux Suppléments.*

do)? Everyone knows the Chinese had invented gunpowder, the Romans the elevator. Perhaps these Tahitians are the last vestiges of a glorious and prosperous society which has had its palaces and its pomps—and which then understood the vanity of such things. Meillet, speaking of languages, remarks that it cannot be established with certitude that any one is nearer its origins than another. In fact there exists no single people one can quite honestly call *primitive.*

"Then," replies Jean-Jacques, "it is enough for me to feel that this primitive man exists within myself. And I know he is good."

"I'm not so sure," says Sade.

I must confess that, as everyone has said, there are too many tortures in *Justine*—and a hundred times more in *La Nouvelle Justine.* Too many strappadoes and rapier cuts, too many gibbets and pulleys, too many rods and whips. Nevertheless, let us not be hypocritical. There exists, in our own European literature, another work, one highly esteemed, which contains (along with pictures) still more tortures than Sade's entire *oeuvre,* and more refinements in the tortures, and more persistence in the refinements: not thirty or forty but a hundred thousand women wrapped in dry straw and burned by slow fires (the women, of course, gagged to muffle their screams); other women thrust upon beds of nails and violated before the eyes of their impaled husbands; princes and princesses slowly roasted over glowing coals; peasant girls in chains (those gentle lambs, as the author calls them) dying of hunger under the lash. At the end of this work it is not by tens (as in *La Nouvelle Justine*) that the victims are numbered, but by millions. Precisely twenty million, according to our author. Moreover, our author is a respectable one; historians (such as Gomara or Fray Luis Bertram) have confirmed his assertions within a few million; for the work in question is not a novel at all, but a piece of pure journalism: the *Brevíssima relación de la destruyción de las Indias* of Fray Bartolomé de Las Casas, whom no one would suspect of attempting to cater to our worst instincts. Nor had the Spanish soldiers who sailed for the New World been chosen for their cruelty. They were merely curious—simple adventurers, like you and me. But after all, whole nations were handed over to them.

That a man might take the keenest pleasure in cutting another
man (or a woman) into pieces, and first—especially, perhaps—
in *imagining* he is cutting him into pieces, is such an obvious
fact that I really do not know what cowardice generally compels
us to conceal it. I really do not know, for ultimately I can see
nothing in this fact to embarrass Christianity—or Mohammed-
anism, or Taoism—in the slightest, all such religious holding
that humanity has at some moment in its history separated itself
from God. And with what justification would the unbeliever
refuse to observe this humanity without prejudice?

It is evident, nevertheless, that he does refuse, as soon as he
finds himself hard-pressed, to construct, and all too cheaply at
that, a natural philosophy—the nineteenth century called it "a
lay morality"—free of laws and authority, free of God. And
from then on, cheating costs him nothing. Which is why Sade
is so precious to us, for he refuses this lie, this cheat. It will be
pointed out that he makes his refusals with a little too much
heat. Oh, Sade is hardly a patient man. And do you think the
others failed to exasperate him, with their ecstasies over nature,
their tears before waterfalls, their raptures at the sight of new
grass? There had to be an antidote to so much inanity.

"An odd antidote," says Justine. "And what kind of life would
I have?"

"An absurd life," answers Sade. "This is how it will be. . . ."

The scene is generally laid in some wild and almost inacces-
sible château, or in some monastery lost in the depths of a forest.
Justine finds herself held captive in a tower with three other
girls: grave Omphale, giddy Florette, and the inconsolable Cor-
nelia, all slaves of perverted monks. Alone? From all appearances there are, within the cloister wall, other towers, and in
them other women. Sometimes one or another of these slaves
disappears. What happens to her? Everything leads us to believe
she leaves both life and monastery behind. Why is she made to
vanish in this way? It is impossible to find out. Age has nothing to do with it. "I have seen," Omphale says to Justine, "a
virgin of seventy kept here while more than twelve girls under

sixteen were sent away." Not age, nor behavior either. "I have seen some who more than responded to *their* desires and who nevertheless left after six weeks; others, sulky and temperamental, were kept here many years." Moreover the girls are well fed, well dressed. If they only knew what to believe, how to behave. . . . But no. "It is no excuse here to say: Don't punish me, I didn't know the law. You are forewarned of nothing, and you are punished for everything. . . . Yesterday you were whipped without having done anything wrong; soon you will be whipped for having really transgressed. In no case must you ever imagine you are innocent." (Thus throughout *Justine* are interwoven the themes of *The Castle* and *The Trial*.) Omphale also says, "it is essential never to refuse anything . . . to expect everything, and even so, however helpful such an attitude may be, you cannot be safe for long."

What remedies for so many evils? Only one. The wretched console themselves with the sight of so many others, equally wretched, around them, so many others tormented by the same riddles—victims of the same absurdity.

It would be naïve to suppose that Sade is concerned, in this story, merely with four lost lambs.

VII. SADE DISAPPOINTED

It was in 1791 that Sade was to have his hour, and his months of triumph. For the Revolution, which hailed him as one of its Fathers, liberated him and honored him. The Théâtre Molière put on his play *Comte Oxtiern;* in the streets the people hummed a cantata to the divine Marat composed by the divine Marquis. The brilliance of his conversation, the range of his knowledge, the virulence of his hatred—everything promised Sade a brilliant and unshadowed career. He differed only slightly, on two or three points,[11] from his new friends: like Marat he wanted a communist state; but he also wanted to maintain a prince who would see to it that the new laws were applied. What was more important, such laws were to be gentle and moderate, the death

---

[11] It seems likely that Zamé's theories, in *Aline et Valcour*, follow Sade's political opinions quite closely.

penalty abolished: if the heat of human passion sometimes justified crime, nothing could excuse its appearance in the civil
codes[12] ". . . which are by definition of a reasonable and objec-
tive nature. Yet these distinctions are delicate enough (he adds)
to escape many who evidently can neither reflect nor even count.
So, good people, you kill one man for having killed another.
Which makes two men the less instead of one."

Thus speaks, at the Section des Piques, and not without insolence, Citizen-Secretary Brutus de Sade. I can almost see him,
hear him. He is a trifle round-shouldered—from the tyrant's dungeons—and he has put on a little weight. Otherwise, the same
noble bearing, the same ardor, with just a dash of servility, and
even smiling.

He smiles, like all disappointed men; for he is disappointed.
It is not everything, in this life, to be free. Misfortunes begin
to rain down on him from all sides. His lawyer, that flea of a
Gaufridy (I use his words), is demanding money; his pigs of
children act as if he didn't exist; his châteaux in Provence are
threatened with demolition, and are being rifled in the meantime. At the Section itself he notices that the citizens are keeping
an eye on him. They expect something more from the ferocious
Marquis. Something more than this assiduity, these cantatas, this
politeness. (When the enemy presses us on all sides, when the
fifth column is ruining us from within; when we are perishing
of hunger. . . .). Then too, Secretary—and even, later on, President—of the Section des Piques is scarcely a suitable situation.
He asks for a library. No answer. The theaters reject his new
plays, which lack, it appears, certain civic virtues. "I'll give
them their civic virtues," Sade growls from behind his President's
desk. At this moment a funny-looking old man walks in: a
former aristocrat who asks (the Secretary says) to be admitted to
the Section; who sits down in a corner; who looks as if he were
doing something in his pants; who turns his cane between his
fingers like an imbecile; it would be a pleasure to clean it off on
his weasel-faced mug. But this is the Président de Montreuil!
The Enemy, the Persecutor to whom Sade owes some thirteen
years in the Bastille.

[12] Cf. *La Philosophie dans le Boudoir; Français, encore un effort . . .*

Now then! But Sade merely steps forward and shakes his hand; cheers him up a little—of course he will be admitted, no need to worry about that. Besides, he musn't think it's very amusing here at the Section every day! (Poor Montreuil, a lot he cares about amusing himself.) Three days later Commandant Ramand, an officer of the Armée de la Somme, appears before Sade. "Have you helped *émigrés* escape?" Sade asks.

"Yes."

"The penalty for such conduct is death, you know."

"Yes, I know," says the brave Commandant.

"Here," Sade says, "here are three hundred pounds sterling and the necessary papers. Now get out of here!"[13] A few days later Ramand is in the provinces and Sade is in Les Madelonettes. If he escapes death in the nick of time, it is only because Robespierre has meanwhile been executed. Besides, he will soon be in prison again: he has written a pamphlet against Josephine. Why a pamphlet, why against Josephine? Doubtless for the same reason that made him welcome Montreuil and release the Commandant.

One turns to the simplest explanation first. In prison Sade had become a writer. Of course he had already tinkered with literature, here and there. A delicate pen, as they say; something in the troubadour line (after all, he came from Provence). But in prison, writing had become a kind of revelation.

It is impossible to suggest, even vaguely, the quantity of this persecuted *oeuvre,* of which we know today not even a fourth. If you would imagine the fury, the rage with which Sade wrote, consider his novel, *Les Infortunes de la Vertu,* for which he patiently works out an elaborate outline and which he writes a first time, then a second, then a third, reworking each detail, correcting, or better still reinventing each phrase; and the second version is twice as long as the first; the third—fifteen hundred pages!—three times as long as the second. It is worse than a vice or a drug; it is more of a passion, a compulsion. Yet as soon as he is liberated, his children, his affairs, everything conspires against this very writing. How can you live while you

---

[13] "They wanted to make me commit inhuman acts. I was never willing to do so." Sade writes in a letter to Gaufridy.

are writing? Parasite, pimp, blackmailer—all means, as we know
too well, are justified if you have to write. And the wretch who
has taken on—to be independent, he says—some "second job"
(but what was the first?) as journalist, civil servant, underwriter,
has only one recourse: to plead disability. Sade, on the other
hand, pleads guilty. Are rebels imprisoned in such a year. Sade
is. Are men of indulgence? "I am quite free, if I please, to let
these fools go." Are conspirators? Why not? Atheists and liber-
tines? "A perfect description of me if ever I heard one." When
all else fails, there is still madness. One could read, one was free
to write—the fury of solitary confinement contributing its share
—in the asylums and prisons of the eighteenth century, which
were mild enough for an aristocrat about whom you never
knew what he had done to be there at all. "And where does this
one come from?" Sade's jailers wondered. "Why is he here?"

"He's supposed to have plotted against God."

"Imagine that!"

Yes, such a reason is plausible enough. But let us look a little
further. A man may pursue fame, love, or freedom with such
energy that he transcends his own purpose—with such keen and
jealous passion that he soon comes to despise his original intent.
And was Glory only this gossip in the papers, Academy elections,
interviews, and a popular song of which no one remembered
the author any more? And was Liberty only this (scattered) ap-
plause from the pit, defiant commendations, votes that would
turn against you tomorrow? No, not even pride could be satisfied with these, but only the lowest kind of vanity. Vanity and
some unaccountable taste for deception, a desire to be cuckolded.
For this is the moment the soul's forces mysteriously change direction: the conqueror discovers himself vanquished by his own
conquest; the lover flees his mistress; penury becomes for the
miser the very symbol of his fortune. The braggart rejoices and
rages alike at the silence his extravagant pretentions create
around him; the lover of liberty returns to prison. Properly dis-
gusted.

Yes, the explanation is plausible. I nevertheless cannot say it
altogether satisfies me. Let us return to our lambs.

VIII. WHICH HAS NOTHING TO DO WITH NATURE

Sadism is unhesitatingly discussed in our newspapers, our serious books. Which is quite appropriate to an altogether spontaneous and natural human characteristic that has been known since the beginning of time and that can, after all, be put into five words: we want to be happy. We also want others to be not quite so happy; which latter impulse we happen to encourage in proportion to our strength. The fact that this characteristic may degenerate, under the burden of circumstances, of nature, even, for all I know, of heredity, is the psychiatrist's problem, not mine. I do not know if Sade was a sadist (in the pathological sense of the term); the trials do not shed much light on the matter; in the one we know most about, at Marseilles, Sade comes off more of a masochist than anything else. At least I can see that he deliberately declined his opportunities to be cruel when everything provided him an occasion for it—his grudges, the passions of the moment, and the Section des Piques to a man. (There is still considerable matter for debate on this point; perhaps the real sadist is the man who rejects sadism's facilities, who permits no one to encourage him in the performance of his obsession. Every man has his pride.) But here is something stranger still.

We have got into the habit, the last fifty years or so, of talking about *masochism* (as I have just done) the same way we talk about sadism. Quite as naturally. As if it were a human characteristic no less simple, no less necessary, and furthermore no less susceptible of becoming an obsession. To which I have no objection. But if masochism is a natural characteristic, we must confess it is indeed a baroque one—one we must have no little good will to call "natural."

Take the eye, for example. I observe that it is subject to more than one anomaly. It may be hypermetropic or myopic; it can present rarer and (like sadism itself) more distinguished defects: amaurosis or diplopia. It can even turn its vices to its own advantage: can be nyctalopic and *content to be nyctalopic* (as the sadist can put his sadism to good use: after all, in a well-regulated society there must also be executioners and prison guards; in

any case, nurses and surgeons; and so much the better for them
if their profession is not too much of a burden, if it provides
them with some pleasure). So far, so good. But never, never has
an eye been discovered to be affected with buzzing or with chro-
matic audition. Yet this, it is claimed, all other things being
equal, is what is to be found in masochism.

That someone else's pain gives me pleasure is obviously a
singular sentiment, doubtless a blameworthy one as well. In any
case a clear-cut and accessible sentiment, one which the *Encyclopédie* can classify in its files; and if the *Encyclopédie* itself,
in a fit of modesty, happens to forget about it, the honest disciple,
emboldened by the glory of his masters, will not. But that my
own pain should be a source of my pleasure, that my *own*
humiliation should be my pride, is neither blameworthy nor
singular, it is merely obscure, making it all too easy to reply: if
pain, it cannot be pleasure; if pride, it cannot be humiliation;
if. . . . Another example will be even more obvious.

I no longer remember which celebrated statesman once
sighed: "Life would be bearable if it were not for its pleasures."
In any case, beneath a paradoxical appearance he was saying
something simple and very precise. It comes down to this, more
or less: what you take for pleasure, what you *call* pleasure, is not
pleasure at all (or at least not for me).

And of course this opinion is open to debate. But it has precisely this merit, that it can be debated. It is coherent, it gives us
food for thought, it is even, perhaps, enthralling. Whereas the
gentleman (or the lady) who comes to us saying "Life would
be unbearable if it were not for its pains"—and not content with
saying so, proves quite emphatically by his conduct that he be-
lieves what he is saying and that this is really the way things are
for him—seems, somehow, to be setting us a riddle, and at first
we want to ask him if he is making fun of everything. "Is it
really true that distress gives you pleasure? That evil does you
good? How strange you are! I suppose the sun seems dark to
you and the night brilliant? Probably your ears see for you, and
your eyes hear—you must be difficult to talk to!"

I acknowledge that the person in question is quite sincere, and
that we are dealing with a real event; perhaps even a

common event. Let us at least agree that if it is normal and common, it is still in the category of a supernatural event, not a law of nature—a miracle, not a phenomenon. And the *Encyclopédie* may try to classify it in its files, but not without some sort of juggling, for nature, after all—or natural law, if you prefer—indicates that pain produces, among others, such and such psychological or physiological effects, such and such arterial tension, such and such pulse rate, etc. Nature also indicates—even before anything else—that pain is pain. That a mouse is a mouse, and a pumpkin a pumpkin. As soon as a pumpkin (as in the fairy tale) happens to be a coach, and the mouse a coachman, we obviously leave the realm of nature for another world, which we must call a magical or supernatural world. Whether the event is common or not does not affect the case. It is readily admitted that poetry is mysterious, and if this is true it must be an extremely common and banal kind of mystery, since at any moment we can open a book of poems. But poetry is no less mysterious for all that.

Now no one will deny, on the other hand, that there exists something which with good reason is known as *masochism*. More precisely, both men and women exist whom we must call *masochists* (if we begin by removing from the word its over-scientific, its—precisely—encyclopedic qualities).

For every day we see those among us who crave nothing so much as raillery and ridicule, and feed on shame and pain in preference to bread and wine. They have their saints, and their heroes. There is Brother Rufinus, who preaches in his church as naked as his mother made him; Saint Philip Neri, who dances in the streets and shaves off only half his beard, for he prefers being thought a madman rather than a saint; Sheik Abderrahman al Madjoud, who castrates himself and crouches out in the desert, winter and summer. And there is no lack of those who wish their friends—and chief among their friends, themselves—"suffering, desertion, disease, ill-treatment, dishonor, profound self-loathing, and the martyrdom of self-distrust."[14] And still others who say with the Portuguese nun: "Let me suffer still more pain." To anyone who remarks that this is all a cunning attempt to insure oneself the good that follows evil—and the honor that follows dishonor—according to some natural law of compensation, we must (politely) reply that he has missed the point. More wisely, the Mohammedans say of their saints (after they have recited their great deeds—or, if you prefer, their follies —in the genre of those we have just described): "And may Allah protect their secret!" It could scarcely be better put, for there actually is a secret, in the purest sense of the word. It is not only a question of an event which is dissimulated, but of an event which cannot *not* be dissimulated; since it is, to be exact, inexpressible. But I shall continue.

We know those others who run to meet vexations and tortures, marvelously forewarned, as if *sensitized* in some organ or other, by the operations of an infallible instinct, to the presence of a possible executioner: fascinated beforehand, summoned—in cases where their neighbor distinguishes only ordinary people of *no special importance*—by these executioners they have divined. Or, who knows, provoking them by their very expectation, by their unconfessed desire. Astonished, nevertheless, by each new torture inflicted upon them, and, like modesty itself, refusing to see what they see, to know what they know, to desire what they desire—to be what they are. Which is the whole story of Justine.

We know of others who bring themselves, of their own accord and with a curious obstinacy, to the place where prison, shame, prosecution and death await them.

IX. SADE HIMSELF, OR THE ANSWER TO THE RIDDLES

Let us no longer claim to shed all the light possible, nor to account altogether for a difficult event—to be precise, for a supernatural event—upon which analysis may well crack its teeth. No, quite the contrary. After all, I understand nothing about such people. And doubtless there is nothing to *understand,* since Sade himself, instead of once and for all explaining himself, confines himself, under the name of Justine, to describing himself and tirelessly itemizing his actions, to elaborating his indictment. Therefore I shall no longer be surprised that the champion

---

14 Nietzsche, *The Will to Power.*

of liberty should seek his own imprisonment, that the man of pride should demand silence, the miser penury, the writer oblivion or disease. (Furthermore, it must be confessed that my explanations just now were, aside from being banal, rather frivolous: for pride, independence, and avarice are after all aware, and aware well in advance, of the signs of glory, liberty, and fortune; and hence quite unjustified in complaining of their lot. As for the writer . . . —but what is the source of this compulsion to write, this irrepressible need, if not some mysterious discovery?) In short, I take the mystery of the matter into consideration. And what is more curious, I immediately find myself rewarded for my modesty. For everything takes its place as if this mystery —for lack of being in itself natural and legal—were an element in a more general law, and, precisely in Sade's case, happened to be provoked by another fact which is very clear and easy to grasp.

Sade, of course, among all these men who have exposed themselves to us, who like Brother Rufinus have stripped themselves naked, was most violently and most continuously the victim of an event which we have had to call antinatural or supernatural. And at this point let us remark, since there is a ridiculous legend of Sade as something of a carefree creature who took life easy, that this man, a man constituted not only by his powerful instincts and his admirable physique, but by a mind obedient to this body to enjoy life and to drain, as we say, the cup of pleasures, was also a man who did everything within his power to call down upon himself (and mysteriously adapt himself to) shame and hatred, desertion and outrage, ultimately presenting the only pure image of despair in all our literature. Not arrogant despair, à la Vigny, nor modest, à la Vauvenargues. No, Sade's despair is shameless and undignified, rather noisy, vulgar. That is his greatness, and we must not minimize it. This author of *romans noirs* is still blacker than his novels. His private correspondence scarcely ever stops abusing his lawyers and blaspheming his friends. When, in his will, he speaks of himself, it is with horror. There is only one object in the world he manages to mention with some tenderness: his dungeon. "The salutary silence," he says, "that I found there. . . ." And if he has not, on that account, become a saint, let us not forget the stubbornness with which the popular tongue (often more just than academies, more daring than poets) has persisted in calling him *divine*. Indeed, if some supernatural event—as we have had to call it—occurred, no one would have experienced it more fully, no one would have been more struck by it than Sade. Yet there is something more.

It is, that of all the philosophers and novelists, Sade is the one who has rejected the supernatural with the greatest rage and fury: rejected every legend and every myth. More positive than the *Encyclopédie,* more coherent than Voltaire, more rigorous than d'Alembert; priding himself—like his heroes—only on his frankness and the exactitude with which he observes his principles; unceasingly putting himself into play, into action, into question; lucid, moreover, as no one else has ever been, yet full of hatred for all those false savants who slyly insinuate into their systems a god whom they claim to eliminate. . . .

A strange experiment. At the end of so obstinate—so heroic —an effort, we find only another mystery: the myth of the Man in the Dungeon, the divine Marquis, the martyr Marquis; the freest mind in the most imprisoned body—Sade, or "a lover of liberty who preferred jails." As if the supernatural, pitilessly outlawed from his books (and from his thought), inevitably took revenge upon Sade himself and, hunted from the work, triumphed in the man. Sade, or the revenge of Magic. Yet I am not willing to say that a mystery can be an explanation. I am only asking myself if a valid explanation can exist that does not take mystery into consideration. I merely see that, without this concession to mystery (to mystery and to its voiceless requirements, its sudden recurrences of strength), Sade will remain perfectly obscure, vague, inconsistent. And not only Sade, but the riddles that haunt him, the riddles he constantly poses to Justine—the riddles he poses to himself.

For so many riddles really constitute only one: is man altogether *natural?* Must we speak of him only as a physicist, following observation and experiment alone, as we do with a stone, a plant, a chemical product? Let us admit, in this case, that each individual is the master of his own body, unique in his proprietorship and in his property, equally betrayed by all religions and moral systems, and having no rule of life except

in proportion to his powers and strength in an absurd and dis-
connected world. Let us admit that if magic, on the other hand,
is inevitable, and with it the supernatural, it is quite natural that
love and pleasure are sometimes confused, that violence and
brutality are generally (as we see) the characteristics of the weak,
not of the strong; that the surest means of grasping pleasure or
love consists of not looking for them at any price; that man,
ultimately, can escape himself and prefers, to what he sees and
feels, what he does not even succeed in altogether imagining:
Gods and myths; that man shows himself—in sadism, to be
exact—a little too preoccupied (dangerously preoccupied) with
the place—the person—in which a mysterious transmutation
takes place. Let us admit that the answer to the various riddles
with which Justine is struggling is Justine herself and Sade—
Sade the man.

Whether man is altogether natural is a very old question, one
of the oldest questions that have divided men among themselves.
And I see quite clearly the answer which Sade has made, with
singular persistence, in his writings: it is perhaps the most curious, certainly the most paradoxical, the most enthralling answer.
But I also see the other answer which Sade makes despite himself, in his body and in his life: and this answer is the contrary
of the other. I am trying only to understand Sade—Sade, and
the exceptional (though half-secret) attention he has aroused. I
should not be disturbed, on such an occasion, if I happened,
not of course to defend, but to understand sadism, however
slightly. And even if my hypothesis is considered frivolous or
absurd, it must be admitted that it is (as the physicists have it)
an excellent working hypothesis. For it illuminates well enough,
at the expense of a single obscure point, I do not say only Sade's
behavior, but that of his heroes, and, primarily, that of his
heroine—of his discreet, modest, fulfilled heroine. In fact, it
even sheds some light on the continual astonishment with which
this monotonous epic affects us, and on that singular effectiveness with which we have been preoccupied. Perhaps, after all,
there are no writers and no heroines worthy of influence except
those who have paid with their own person for the answer to

the (perhaps too vast) problems which they undertook to solve; and we must therefore take our choice—Nietzsche, Pascal, Rimbaud, Sade—among madness, insignificance, death or prison.

THE ACCOMPLICE

There exists a curious book by Crébillon, *Les Lettres de la Marquise de M . . .* , in which tenderness and jealousy, the need for love and the reluctance to surrender to love, desire and coquetry, are depicted with great care, without the reader's once knowing for sure whether the Marquise and the Count have slept together. *Les Infortunes de la Vertu* poses just the opposite problem. Justine's extremely diverse, extremely involuntary sexual experience is represented in the greatest detail without our ever obtaining the slightest suspicion—desire, love, horror, indifference—of what our heroine might be feeling. Actually, it was difficult to say. As Sade knows only too well. Only too well, since he is Justine.

Justine's strange secret is that she too is joyous; that she is delighted and fulfilled by the misfortunes she calls down upon herself. That much is clear. And all in all, what makes the secret difficult for us is not that it cannot be named; no, quite the contrary. It is because it has already been named; it is even because it has been named a little too often, with the name of that good Austrian novelist who came into the world a hundred years after Sade and whose cruel heroines are furnished with a riding crop and sometimes with a fur cloak.

It is time for a change of names: I am well aware that all tastes and all compulsions can be found in nature. Masochism is neither more dangerous nor more offensive than another. And no less. But it is more mysterious! It is precisely the one compulsion which cannot be contradicted without being encouraged, nor punished without being rewarded. Perfectly incomprehensible: supernatural or, if you prefer, absurd.

Nevertheless, out of this absurdity the critic, as the saying goes, can make some sense for himself.

—Translated by Richard Howard

GEORGE MOORSE
Palo Pego

Palo Pego being a very rare Puerto Rican root which if you take
it in rum after a good soak will help you or maybe not of course
depending on how much help you need which may not even be
the case but usually is. If you try to pick it up in a bodega they
will tell you that this is the wrong season or the shipment didn't
get through customs or the salesman got burnt by his No. 3
wife hot in from Lake Como or anything to make you believe
that it would be much easier to buy it in Algeria or Uzbekistan
than in N. Y. which is probably true and who cares. It is yel-
lowish and not convincingly innocent-looking. Ladies love it.
It excerebrates them.

Red took it in rum—Palo Viejo—on an August evening. She
said "Twisted!" and slid into a modern-dance position. I loped
across the room to her, smelling of garbage and wheezing. The
telephone rang, shattering a pane of stained glass in my forehead.
Red was moaning, but I answered the phone and Jose said:
"Have you seen Red?"

GEORGE MOORSE, whose short story "The Hat" appeared in *New World
Writing 19*, was born in New York in 1936. His poems and articles were
published in various American periodicals until 1957, when he moved to
Europe. At present he lives in Munich, where he has completed one short
novel and is at work on a second.

"No."

She moaned some more and I hung up. A few minutes later the phone rang again and Red said "Oohooom," but I crawled away from her and toward it whispering "It might mean money!" but it was Jose again and he said "Liar!" in a way that made the putty crumble out of the window frame in my forehead, and then he hung up. Back to Red again. She said "Oohooom" again. She needed no more Palo Pego.

By two o'clock the next afternoon I didn't know anyone, including Red and myself, who hadn't lost a job. The sun was shining and I even bathed. It was no strain to go to a C movie on the East Side with the professionally unemployed Greek couple in the next apartment or to end up the day spending my last money on cab fare to the beach to see if the tide was really rising. In the hurricane wind lots of beach parties and foam and fireworks. The apex of a consummately joyous simian day.

That was the week the Coast Guard had to dynamite a stranded sperm whale in the inlet.

Thirty pacifists and five hundred sea gulls perched on the rotting corpse despite armed guards and the reek of unprocessed ambergris.

Messrs Madig and Riparotis, Vice Pres. and Pres. respectively of the Bone Beach Co., appeared far enough from the scene to have to employ 150x binoculars to view it.

"How much we paying them buggers to sit on the whale?" Riparotis asked.

"Got 'em free," Madig said. "One phone call."

"And the birds?"

"Had to drug 'em with laudanum, but could only get two hundred onter the thing. The rest is stuffed."

Riparotis adjusted his binoculars.

"Here come the reporters."

Flash bulb lightning. Madig leafed through a pocket calendar. "Cops arrive at three to remove the anarchists. Whale detonated at three thirty. More pictures. Newsreel. Your double will be there. Sunburn-girls . . . indecent exposure. Boy Scout mourning parade four o'clock. Repeal telegram from Albany also at four, Coast Guard protest note four fifteen, the Pres——"

"How much this costing us, Vincent?"

"No sweat." Madig casually bored a gloved finger into a nostril. "We sell ninety thousand lobsters and twice as many plastic whales. We gotta balance. July it rained, Spiros!"

I finished polishing the hub caps and went back to work in the garbage dump.

It was the very same week that the life guards constructed a still in one of the B.B. Co.'s storage rooms and swung into the nightly bars barefoot drunk and dancing with girls who exposed their untanned bosoms and whistled bebop between their teeth. The towns and beaches were filled with savage echoes of lust. (Echoes which come to me isolated now like collar buttons rolling across a linoleum floor, a thousand permutations of shape and size and sound and smell typified by hot-rod backfires in suburban streets, lascivious mournful moans under horse blankets at smelly low tide, or the polished stocks and barrels of Daisy air rifles.) A vast emergency in my vibrating internal two-way universe. Mockery of war, peace, stop watches and skeletal umbrellas.

Nude swimmers plopped into the hurricane waves like Brancusi birds of polished bronze, came up again like seals, flashed back to the tidewrack to drink beer from cans and shake off the water in big drops.

Jose and Red and I.

Days filled with an odor worse than the exploding whale: American garbage under the sun . . . because daylight began and ended for me in the main garbage dump among the dunes. For Jose, too. Red worked in the central office, another sort of garbage dump.

We were all hired by Mr. Petrus Borel, Gen. Man. of the B.B. Co. and part-time werewolf.

"Uster have a machine did that work but it got eat up by all them horrible chemicals down there, get what I mean? You boys miss the chance of a long impoverished lifetime when you don't grab this here job with all fours. Get what I mean? I mean, you get it?"

"Sure," we said like the Corsican brothers.

"All yer gotta do rake through the garbage for soda bottles

with them big rakes and stack up them soda bottles in them big
crates and you get paid. Plenty." His neck twitched in a phony
admiral's collar. "Off yer go, lads! Get me?"

When darkness came he pranced around the main office slav-
ering and baying at the moon or even at the neon lamp and
pawing Red around the knees, and the thighs, and the back, and
the shoulders, and the breasts, and the arms, and the neck, and
the face, and sometimes around the toes, the stomach, the brows,
the fingertips or the heels.

"You're all mine tonight, dolling!"

Red squirmed. But she might even have liked it.

She was a sort of receptionist type. Whereas Jose claimed she
was beautiful muy bonita and Mr. Borel treated her like an extremely delicate and juicy bifsteak anglais, I merely enjoyed
liking her and when it eventually got around to liking enjoying
her that was okay too, but I was naif and baboonish that summer
and the whole world was Wild Rat Country to me, and I rarely
changed my socks and when I did it was to put on old ones I
found covered with fuzz in a corner, and I made fun of old ladies
and fat pimply adolescent girls on the streets, copied down the
phone numbers in johns and often called them ("There ain't no
Agnes here, doll, but you sound like a thwell fellow come up
some time have a couple of quarts of the most fabulous Mon-
golian applejack!"), stole obtuse theological treatises from the
public library and sniffed the oxblood breath of lonely lady
dentists in the week-end dawn.

"I dream of Red forever and foralways," Jose said as we rode
to work. "We all go swimming tonight man, you leave her to me.
I can't wait." His eyes glowed and shook around in his narrow
sunburnt head. "I fix you up with Sue, okay?"

"The blonde one? Emaciated? Twin brother carries a sawed
off shotgun?"

"The very same."

"It's Tuesday night, what can I say. Tuesday I always think is
gonna be the last day before I change my life and go to Australia
and become a pioneer. She's ah sinewy."

"Yeah," Jose said.

"Red on the other hand is like a ripe apricot. And lithe."

"Yeah, lithe," he giggled. "The way she swishes! The way she switches! The way she swatches and flitches and flatches!" He nearly fell out of the jeep. Borel, at the wheel, grunted lycanthropically and spat into the wind.

Only sign of life on the road to the dump wasn't really that at all, and you had to look carefully to see it. The rest was desert. Like in a 1943 escaped POW movie with gunshots and SS uniforms with an existentialist ending. Sand and saw grass. Borel, in an Orlon admiral's uniform, drove with an archaic hatred for deserts and jeeps and snarled to himself:

". . . salt of the earth . . . knockneed drunkards and adolescent zombies don't know a employment office from a line-up . . . do nothin' but pick their toes and read *Das Kapital* in comic-book form . . ."

He drove like a sonabitch, and his fat voice faded into jeep backfires and the sea-sound on the other side of the dunes. Music to my ears.

We could smell the dump already.

"When you boys get picked up?" Borel's sunburnt face looked like a ball of congealed petroleum.

"Six?"

Jose rolled his eyes. "Told Red five thirty—" he whispered. Masochist.

"Seven," Borel said.

"Huh?"

"Jose!" I said. "You got a college edication! You gonna let this jerk keep us in pecuniary serfdom already? Twelve hours in the blazing sun without a Drop of Water?"

"*SEVEN!*" Borel barked, slamming the keep into climbing gear and pointing it at a story-high hungover sand dune. "No savvy Inglezzy?! Goldbrickers and time-clock freaks! Give ya bastards a concession any male citizen'd give his left tentacle for and yer wanna taxi service yet! I go through this way seven o'clock on my way back from the storehouse and——"

Jose tumbled shrieking out of the jeep and cartwheeled down the dune to vanish in weeds and charred driftwood. Borel played cha-cha-cha on the gas and I followed, picking up a mouthful of flea-y sand on the way down. He circled once and threw our

lunch packages over his shoulder into the jeep tracks. Then he
was gone.

Jose and I met over a rusty piece of tin. We were both spitting
sand.

"I hope they devaluate the dollar," Jose said.

The garbage dump is a little less than a mile wide and is always burning somewhere. Black-brown smoke floats up toward
the top of the clean August sky like filthy curdled cream. Unspeakable odor that grabs the stomach and stabs the nostrils and
lungs. A thoroughly bubonic atmosphere.

The whole dump is divided in partes tres. The two parts which
we work and the third part, which is usually burning. Often the
whole thing is burning. We have one flat wooden wagon with
baby-carriage wheels, two long rakes and about a hundred empty
crates for the bottles. And of course the rats. There are more
rats than anything except flies, and there are considerably more
flies than garbage.

Fifteen cents mex is paid out for every crate we fill with usable
bottles, and we fill so many crates a day that we are planning to
hop jets to Teneriffa at the end of the summer and invest in real
estate there.

Largely we collect beer bottles and bottles warped by the fires.
They aren't considered usable.

The dump is all knolls and hills and holes, a smoldering battle
landscape where glass mines explode on your birthday and
goggle-eyed basket cases of World War III rattle through the
rubbish in bomb-proof robot wheelchairs, obsolete doughboys in
gas masks with 200-lb packs drop grenades into bunkers, throw
out smoke screens, crawl through snagging barbed wire and shout
in Flemish as tunnels cross fifty feet under the lines and les
boches loot the wine cellars and hallucinatory whore houses
creak by on iron wheels and Charlie Chaplin dances like a
lunatic around one of Big Bertha's shells. War! War! Garbage
produced by the men who know how, faster than you can sift
it! Moldy hot dogs, orange peels, coffee grounds and cobalt flash
bulbs leaving nothing but your shadow on the wall!

"I prefer the Katzenjammer Kids to Flash Gordon," says Jose, leafing through stained Sunday pages.

Tell the truth, we work about three hours a day. The rest of the time we sit in the shade of a dune reading comic books and smoking cigarettes. Like me, Jose is a lazy bastard. Fish never got farther than the shoals. Why did he quit N.Y.U. to seek gainless employment in the dumps? Why did he put on powder-blue zoot suits and sing like Billie Holliday in a chalk-and-fingernail falsetto? Why was he consumed with something that might even have been love for Red?

Jose: (in the pose of a New Wave movie star) "Moi, jm'en fou. Haha. Tu. Sale con."

Couldn't get another answer out of him.

Though we were pretty good friends, I couldn't figure him out too well, but then I didn't think very much, especially about other people.

He was mad about Red. In that nightmare pit that flimmered and smoked he talked to me about her over his comic book. He described in prurient detail every inch of her body and the inside of her head. She was reeeal smot, he said.

Q: How was Jose on the line? A: The most I'd ever seen him with was an awfully skinny Nordic type—on the Boardwalk one night—an extremely haggard creature with insulin-shock eyes and mail-order beads around her neck. Dear Sue.

One evening Jose slipped a note across the switchboard desk so that one corner of it was pointing exactly at Red's navel—hidden to be sure at the moment by a cashmere sweater. The note read:

> Western wind when will thou blow?
> The small rain down can rain—
> Christ, if my love were in my arms
> And I in my bed again!

—Red tucked it into her handbag.

"Never know who you'll have to blackmail," she said, and Mr Borel sniffed around the office, his fangs and facial hair growing. That night Red had to escape over the tin roof and was driven almost all the way home by one of the alcoholic life guards. She lost the note.

But she actually did make the swimming date with Jose. He mooned about it all afternoon. Miserable hot day. About ten crates full. Four o'clock in the afternoon Borel drives to the dune top with Pres.'s Madig & Riparotis, to view our work. No detail escapes them. They're wearing general's field fatigues, puttees, sun helmets. Red Cross flag on the jeep and two newspaper correspondents crouched on the spare. Riparotis' face like a Greek comedy mask behind the binoculars.

RIPAROTIS: They're throwing bottles at the rats!

MADIG: All work and no play makes Jack a dull boy. Whew!

BOREL: Eau de cologne, sir?

MADIG: Ephedrine, Borel! Ugh! Back to HQ!

RIPAROTIS: Hmmmm . . . Must be some way of converting all that nasty ratty garbage into wholesome edible tidbits. Artificial olives, maybe? Peasants'd never know the difference!

MADIG: Haugh! Houff! Cough!

BOREL: Courage, sir!

RIPAROTIS: Give 'er steam, Borel. And write down their names. I want the salaries cut. Goofing off on company time!

BOREL: Yes, sir!

Five minutes after they left we loaded all the filled crates at the far end of the dump, broke up a couple of empties and set the boards with the clean nails pointing up on the hard-packed sand road Borel would take when he came to pick us up at seven. We scattered fine sand over them and went away whistling over the dunes toward the ocean. Borel had one spare on the jeep and he was lucky if he got off with three flats. It took us an hour and a half to walk back to the central office and it would take him twice as long if he didn't fall into the booby-trapped garbage or explode with loathsomeness under way. In any case we didn't plan to see him again that evening. We made a beeline for Red.

"The way she switches!" Jose said. We gawked through the central office window.

Red was the sort of girl who has to walk a little bit sideways, and who makes high-school English teachers with three kids and a mortgage slip on sunglasses and start the TV scout routine.

(Jose's image.) I say she was all right.

A stool supported a large per cent of the part of Red which among the Hottentot women is called the steatopygia and which among the latter confines the accumulation of body fat, allowing the rest of the body relatively free for whatever movements Hottentot women cultivate, probably not however the identical movements cultivated by Red which were (when on duty): plugging in plugs, and unplugging plugs, and pulling switches, and answering, and delivering greetings, and salutations, and farewells, on the telephone.

Off duty her movements varied.

Quarter of six the three of us were slouching across the cooling sand carrying cartons of beer cans and smiling at the ocean. Red was pretty in her working-girl clothes. On the concrete steps of an umbrella stand Sue was waiting for us, her bony kneecaps up around the lobes of her ears.

"I feel like getting twisted," she said, and there were four of us making for a private-type spot. The sun set. The sky filled with gentle juke-box colors and seagulls squawked by overhead, gliding, hanging on the wind with motionless feathers. A half-track beach sweeper rumbled by with dimmed lamps.

"We cut out of this crummy place, Red," Jose was saying. "We make it to Bermuda and beat tin cans and grow midget potatoes. We do something, baby."

Red bit a bright red lip, almost but not quite thoughtfully. One brow rose. Dostoevski wrote all about that.

"I wanna get twisted," Sue drooled.

"Get *what?*" I said.

"Twisted *and* that," she cackled like the witch in a Dahomey folktale.

Red was already down by the water, peeling, shy and shameless by turns. I watched. Jose was knee deep in water, sputtering and fever-trembling as the waves hit him. Thick hurricane waves.

"I'm getting sick!" Jose said as I splashed close to him.

"Cholera from the rats! Haha!"

I went under, thrashed up a few feet away. The sky was crazy, splashed with light, and Red passed us, her hair soaked black and her big round breasts bobbing in the salty swell. Way back on the dim line of beach Sue stood with one toe in the water, like a scrawny naked voodoo doll.

"Not that!"

"Control yourself," I said, swimming out. The surf made horrible crashing noises behind us. Suddenly Red swept toward me laughing and our bodies smacked together in the breach of a wave.

"Woo!" she shouted.

In a few seconds we're yards apart. She is to my right and Jose is beside her acting as polite as possible under the circumstances. I let a big mean gray wave take me away. The surf booms. Back of me voodoo doll seems to be praying to the moon, one elbow pointing toward Montauk Point and the other toward Times Square. After another breaker I peek and see that she's just guzzling—getting twisted. Jose and Red about a quarter of a mile away now, still close but probably not contiguous. Talking! I swallow cold black water and feel the fever take my body. Now we're a dozen yards apart again and I hear them having a nice conversation in silver-anniversary tones. Jose looks like a haberdasher's dummy.

"... can't flake a ... civet dust ... flannel ..."

"... Micky Mountain oil ... newt! ... operated a ... solfeggio ..."

I swim in and slap the water out of my ears. Beyond the snaking white line of surf their heads still bob, their mouths still wag. I hate myself for wanting to know what language they're speaking.

I went back to the horse blanket and sat down beside voodoo doll. My teeth chattered as I dried off. She smirked. We sat there naked smoking damp cigarettes and passing a bottle back and forth while Jose and Red gossiped in forty feet of water. I didn't even play footy with Sue. It was overpoweringly stupid. When about half the rum was gone she began to disintegrate. I was afraid she was going to pitch on her back and start flapping like a mackerel.

She just passed out. I covered her up and went for another dip.

When I returned her eyes looked strange. I had the feeling that this was the real thing.

"Grrrrr—" she said, foaming at the chops. "I'm twisted, honey. Hows about a little ole——" She crouched there, an enormous aluminum grasshopper. Her thighs glistened and her wee small teats tinkled like a pair of silver bells. "It's it," she whispered. "P-a-l-o P-e-g-o . . ."

In seven telegraphic words that sawed off the top of my head, she explained it completely. One finger indicated a rice-paper package at the corner of the blanket. Now Sue was coiled very tight. I wished I felt more maidenly.

"Zzzzzzzzzzz!"

Something hairy and vaguely human stumbled through the darkness to our left. I could smell its doggy interfemoral breath. It gibbered, snarled, and I knew it must be Borel, on his way back to the central office to tell Madig and Riparotis what nasty garbage diggers we were.

"Gik-gik-gik-gik——"

I pointed Sue at him and let go. She slipped out of my hands with a shampoo squeak, twittered slightly and went off across the sand after Borel. No sound for a long time. Then an outraged sobbing howling moan beyond the dunes in the distance—maybe a bronchial sea gull.

After another dip and a quick frolic in the surf Red and Jose and I got dressed and started back toward the parking field. No one mentioned Sue. Jose and Red had a good deal to say to each other, though. They had a real lovers' argument, though neither of them seemed to know it.

"When I say I like to drink it has nothing to do with if I can drink or not!"

"Hell! You talk to me as if I'm the one who can't take booze!"

Three quarters of the way back they began to fling wet sand at each other. Then Red ran off crying into the dunes and Jose stood staring at the sea, short and dark and tight-lipped, the stench of garbage gone from him.

Then in a moment he was off, screaming her name. Surf slammed. I wanted the city again, and sleep.

Except for the driver and a snoring sailor I was alone on the bus. A long colorless trip . . . until Red climbed on in some ugly empty Long Island town. She noticed me when she paid, came up to my seat, pressed a finger to her lips and sat down beside me. She must have been driven that far by one of the life guards. I didn't ask where Jose was. That was okay.

Wrapped in rice paper in my pocket the Palo Pego fizzed . . . Sure now neither of us needed it . . . Off the bus at Queens Plaza . . . down-a-down into iodine tunnels to wait for an express . . . Bought rum at the all-night liquor store on Cooper Square and then both went up and went to bed. It was about time.

Four days later. Jose comes after me with a wicked pair of tailor's shears in his belt and one of those two-inch fighting knives rolled up in his right fist. I try to explain it to him very coolly, but I am way down within myself and he is too, and we are speaking to each other across the Whitestone Bridge in a thunderstorm, blindfolded, with our mouths full of popcorn.

"She's a great piece of tail!" I shout at last.

Jose's eyes turned into decorated eggshells, cracked in a million pieces, dissolved leaving vermillion holes. Little fish of dirt swam through his head.

"You," he said finally, indicating the remains of the root on the table.

"Me."

"Sonabitch!"

He stuck the shears into the hard wood table and sunk the whole knife blade in beside them and spat and left the room without another word. He stepped over the silk thing on the kitchen floor. He thumped down the stairs like a 19th-century hero. Then he left the building, the city, the country. I never saw him again.

But I did see Red.

Last time on a November night. Things were very cozy but afterwards she told me that in about a month she was marrying somebody I never heard of. They were going to invest in a lawnmower.

"You expected maybe Borel?" she laughed.

"Sure I did, but this is okay too."

"You're almost as smart as Jose."

She showed me a post card she'd received from him. Jose's typical noncommittal way of saying he was having a lousy time. Life is miserable as hell, etc. He had settled down and got some humiliating job in San Juan, Puerto Rico. "Your darling Jose," it was signed.

Right around that time the Palo Pego began to get scarce.

FREDERIC RAPHAEL
The Day Franco Came

"The Day Franco Came" is dedicated to
Harry and Charlotte Gordon.

"Don Antonio——"

"Another time, woman."

"Don Antonio——"

"Did you not hear me? Another time, I said. Later. Another time."

"But when, Don Antonio? When? You always say——"

"Later in the day, woman. This morning I have more important things to do than listen to you. Much more important."

"Don Antonio——"

"Some other time. I'm late now. You know very well, in the mornings——"

"It's impossible ever to speak to you, Don Antonio," said Carmela.

FREDERIC RAPHAEL was born in Chicago, Illinois, in 1931, but has lived in England for most of his adult life. Educated at Charterhouse and St. John's College, Cambridge, Mr. Raphael has six novels to his credit, including *The Limits of Love* and, most recently, *Lindmann.* He is fiction critic for the London *Sunday Times.*

"Very well, it's impossible. You've worked in this house long
enough," said Don Antonio, "long enough to know why I never
have time to waste."

"But, Don Antonio——"

"Shall I tell you why I'm particularly busy this morning? Shall
I? Tell me, what do you think this is?" Don Antonio waved a
blue envelope so thick that it clicked as he flapped it. He held it
an inch from his cook's withdrawn face. "I'll tell you what it is.
This is an official letter from the Military Governor. You know
what that means? You think after getting a letter like this I have
time to waste listening to your complaints about Paco's meat?"

"It's not that, Don Antonio."

"Whatever it is, it must wait."

Carmela passed her hands in front of her face, touching her
nose, her chin, in controlled despair. "Don Antonio——"

"Not now." The Mayor of Torreroja unsheathed his yellow
malacca cane from the umbrella stand against the wall of the
vestibule. "You have no idea of my responsibilities. I certainly
don't expect to be bothered by people in my own household, at
times like these——" The blue letter clicked again. "I'll tell you.
The Caudillo himself is coming to Torreroja. The Caudillo.
The Head of State."

"I know," said Carmela.

"You *know*? How do you know? I didn't know myself until
this morning."

"I know," said Carmela, "that the Caudillo is the Head of
State."

"Now perhaps you understand why I have no time to waste
on domestic nonsense. Do you realize by any chance that the
entire responsibility for making this village respectable in time
for the Caudillo's visit depends exclusively, *exclusively,* on me,
on the Mayor, and on no one else? Do you?"

"Yes, yes." Carmela tightened the string around the waist of
her ballooning black dress. "Yes, yes, yes, but——"

"I have no time for domestic trivialities." Don Antonio tapped
the ferrule of his cane on the tile floor of the hall and turned
for the door. It was a massive double door, wide enough to admit
a horse and cart. Within it, on the left-hand leaf, was cut a

second door, of the normal size, with its bottom a foot above the level of the floor. As Don Antonio approached, the knocker on the outside was lifted and allowed to drop, gently. It was the knock of someone who was expected.

Don Antonio withdrew into the recess incised for the door of a side room. In this room, which was in virtual darkness, the creaking of a cane rocking chair alone indicated someone's presence. Doña Elisabeta, the Mayor's mother, sat invisible but for a pencil of light which ruled her from the crown of her white head down to the buttons on her black boots, between which an ebony stick went to the floor. The pressure imparted by her crossed hands on the silver head of the stick rocked her chair in the darkness. Don Antonio waved Carmela to the door. "Come along, come along."

"Antonio, is that you? Antonio?"

"Yes, Mother, it's me. Only me."

Doña Elisabeta could sit in the dark and imagine a house full of her children. "Antonio, is that you?" she would call, as if it might have been Jaime, María, Pepe, José, Sandro or Pia, or as if it might have been the Colonel himself, Colonel Alfredo Francis Xavier Martín de Córdoba y Albeñiz, whose presence she sensed on the threshhold of her room.

"I'm about to go out, Mother."

"Go with God."

"Yes, Mother."

"Antonio," said the old woman to herself. "Yes." There was the chink of a rosary. "Jaime, María, Pia, Sandro . . ."

Don Antonio frowned. The wounds of the victors should be forgotten. To grieve was to have lost. Still, had he himself not given Torreroja its Garden of Remembrance? Ah, but he didn't sit in the dark calling the roll of the dead. "The Caudillo is coming to Torreroja," he called through the door.

"Praise be to God."

"I am in charge of the arrangements."

"Clearly," said the old woman. "Who else but a man whose father campaigned at his side?"

"Come along, woman, what are you doing?" said Don Antonio to Carmela as she scuffed past in her black slippers. The big iron key snapped back the bolt on the brown door. A mat of sunshine fell on the black and white tiles of the vestibule.

The visitor was a young man with a pale, freckled face, broad shoulders, some stomach and bandy legs. His eyes were narrow behind shell-rimmed glasses. Stepping over the base of the door, he spread his eyelids to recover his vision. He had books under his arm and a white skull cap on his head.

"Good morning, Mr. Stern." Don Antonio was looking at his watch. "My son is waiting for you."

"I've been correcting his exercises," Adam Stern said.

"He is a clever child, Mr. Stern. But, of course, in a village like this—you can imagine what the schooling is like. He has had little chance to develop as he should. That is why I am so glad that you have come to live among us. You can enlarge his world, help him to make the most of his talents. He's progressing, I trust?"

"Oh, yes, indeed."

"Once he really begins to grasp a subject, he will learn very quickly. He is an exceptional boy. Of course, his mother's death——" Don Antonio frowned. Carmela was standing in the patio door. Don Antonio came closer to Adam Stern. "It affected him very badly. A tragedy of that kind—it goes without saying. It was a great shock. Then living here, a village of this kind where the people are ignorant, superstitious—well, you must go to your work and I must go to mine." Don Antonio clicked his blue envelope. "Francisco is waiting upstairs. A clever child can always catch up if you keep him off the streets away from the rabble, isn't that so? Of course, it's entirely in your hands, how you go about it. I pay you well and I leave it to you. I have complete confidence in you, of that you can be sure. After all, with three degrees from American universities, the boy couldn't be in better hands in Madrid itself, isn't that right?" Don Antonio had the door open to the street now; he swung it back and forth using the key as a handle. The sun-shafts sawed at the umbrella stand. "Now if you can help him make up the ground he's lost, if you can get him to the university eventually, if you can——" The Mayor broke off. "Have you nothing to do, woman? No work to do?"

"I am waiting," said Carmela, "to close the front door for you, Don Antonio, when you go out."

"Insolence," the old woman hissed in the darkened room. "Insolence." She pushed her weight on the head of her ebony cane. The rocking chair squeaked. "Insolent servants, insolent, insolent."

"Find something to do. I can shut the door. Go away and find something to do."

"Yes."

"Go along, go along. Servants! No, the trouble with people in this village is they have no idea how civilized people live. How can Francisco have anything in common with them? Do you know I saw the children drinking urine in the street the other day? Drinking the urine, can you believe it? They don't want to be civilized. How can I let Francisco out with children like that? A child as sensitive as he is? If people behaved as these people do where I come from, in the north that is, well—my mother would tell you. People down here have no conception of civilized behavior."

Carmela's broom brought her into view at the patio door.

"Well, I'm late now. I have a great many things to arrange." The Mayor held up his blue envelope. "Official duties."

In the street, Adam Stern could hear the simmering of children's laughter.

"Even when schools are provided, you can't make them go. Now what are they up to? Thank heavens Francisco doesn't have to run about in the street like a wild animal."

Don Antonio appeared high on the heel of his front door. His black brows were joined and the jut of his chest made a turret for his house from the top of which his eyes glared furiously. The fire was withdrawn from the children. Their laughter sagged and they looked up in silence at the Mayor whose stick was over them. They were standing in a tight circle, and Don Antonio, even with his extra height, could not really see what was going on in the center of the cauldron.

There was a blurt of laughter. It came from the one child who seemed not only unintimidated, but actually unaware of Don Antonio. This was a girl, taller than her playmates, who wore a ragged dress, quite sleeveless and much too short for her. She had thin, bent legs and scabby knees, a narrow chest and a neck the stalk of which looked barely strong enough to support her head. Her feet crabbed at the pebbles in the road bed. She lifted her blank face to Don Antonio, revealing two broken teeth among the rotten set behind her torn lips. Her eyes were flat black buttons in the white slice of her face. Her hair, clotted with dirt, hung over her ears and was chopped unevenly at the back. The sleeve holes of her creased cotton dress were so tight that Don Antonio could see the stubs of hair in her armpits. Yet her chest was that of a small girl, without the barest swell of a breast or the prick of a nipple. She gobbled her laughter at Don Antonio and the humor of the other children began to bubble once more behind their nostrils.

The girl pointed. "Umpump."

Don Antonio craned his neck. For the moment he could see only the back of a spotted dog, pink skin under a white coat blotted with black. The children spread into an avenue. Now he saw that the high back of the spotted dog was due to the bitch beneath him. She was a short-legged, shaggy mongrel which loafed about the street. She had been disowned by the barber, José Poblet, on the corner. She stood now with an air of bewildered acceptance. Her back end was lowered and she looked around at it from time to time, the more frequently as the rocking of the dog grew in intensity and his forelegs, laced about her, grabbed higher and more convulsively for their purchase.

"Umpump."

Giggles went off like firecrackers among the children. The bitch and her mate ground on. The spotted dog stretched his neck along the back of the bitch and worked energetically. Presently she too began to stir herself. They staggered forward a step or two. The two faces hung one above the other, mutely bored. A slow tear unfolded from the corner of one of the bitch's eyes. The Mayor swung his cane, scattered the children, made for the dogs.

"Get away, get away, you filthy beasts. Get away."

The dogs, with sideways eyes only acknowledging him, humped and stretched until now, now surely, the dog, making a long neck over the female, came.

"Get away." Don Antonio let his cane into them. "Go on."

The dog unlatched his forelegs and struggled off the bitch, but the pink tassel of his penis still tied him to her. He remained, however he turned, immovably fast.

"Get away from here."

The dogs fell back from Don Antonio as he swung at them again.

"Umpump," pointed out the girl, crouching down like a mechanic.

The other children ran all over the street, as if released from a pen, giggling and dancing and slapping at each other. Don Antonio stamped his foot at the dogs, who collapsed round a corner, reluctant and snarling. He turned on the children: "Will you be quiet and get away from here? Do you want me to fetch Don Leonardo? My son isn't idle garbage like you. He's working at his lessons. He's learning something." Don Antonio pointed to the window of the schoolroom. Was there the skirt of a shadow moving away from the window? The shutter door was away from the glass, opening a slice of opacity. No, much more likely Francisco was sitting in his place at the table, his scrubbed knees neat beneath his knickerbockers, his socks—his English woolen socks—turned over the elastic garters at the top of his shins, his buckled shoes resting on the wooden slat which shackled the ankles of the desk. As for his face, that sensitive face so like his mother's in its olive detachment (so Don Antonio saw his son), and its slightly pouty lips, full yet bloodless, flesh of the same olive, it would be turned attentively on the American professor. "You should all be at school, learning something. How old are you?"

"Six."

"You're not."

"I am."

"He's the sixth. Not six years."

"You should all be at school."

"Too old," said a boy scarcely up to Don Antonio's waist.

"My son is almost fourteen, almost fourteen, but he's at school. That's where you should be. Now get out of this street. My son's trying to work."

They trotted away. The girl, however, stood in Don Antonio's path. He dodged her and strode, chest out, along the lumpy road towards the Plaza. He whipped round and raised his cane at the children, who had re-formed around his front door. They scattered, fresh giggles. The girl was motionless.

At the top of the street, by the market, Don Antonio wheeled once more. The children had run to the far end of the road, down by the *carretera,* where a new foreign car had arrived (anything foreign, Don Antonio thought, and they run), but the girl was still by the house. Don Antonio clapped his cane against the side of his shoe and went about on his heel.

"Good morning, Don Antonio," they began. "If later when you're not busy——"

"Yes, yes, later, later."

"Good morning, Don Antonio, if you have a moment——"

"Not now, not now."

"Don Antonio, you're a busy man, I know——"

"I am indeed and particularly this morning——"

"Don Antonio, I realize your responsibilities, but if later in the day, some other time convenient to yourself——"

"Yes, yes, very well, later on."

Don Antonio's office did not lead him to associate himself as closely as one might have supposed with Torreroja itself. It put him rather above the villagers; he was one not with them but with the régime. As Mayor appointed by Madrid, he was part of Madrid. If he taxed and bullied the Torrerojans, it was not for his private gain or satisfaction, it was to impose upon them a proper sense of humility and obedience. The more heavily he bore upon them (his expenses were considerable), the more sedulously did he hold himself to be doing his duty. If the new café he was in the process of erecting was likely in the end to take custom from the Casino and from the smaller bars in the village, that was Torreroja's bad luck: everyone knew what Torreroja had been. The more he enriched himself, the more powerful was Madrid in the life of the people, the more staunchly did he represent the master whose imminent arrival was proclaimed in the blue envelope which he clasped, like an Order, against his chest.

Don Antonio had a number of appointments that morning, and it was almost noon by the clock on the tower of the new church (the destruction of the old one was but a single instance of what Torreroja had done) before he was able to start along the main road on his way to see how work was progressing on the café. He had first to pass the bar where the gypsies congregated.

"See how his cock's growing," said one of them as he went by.

The Mayor had decided to name his café The Cock, but the gypsy's reference was, without a doubt, to the tall tower which would, on completion, allow Don Antonio to advertise the presence of his Bar–Restaurant for several kilometers in either direction. This tower was growing higher and higher, and as it grew so did the volume of comment it excited. Don Antonio had already had Manolo sack one laborer for alluding to it as "the Mayor's prick," and now the gypsies, filthy animals that they were, had picked up the joke. They could say what they liked; he would teach them a lesson eventually. He had had enough of their impudence already. Their "King," Don Ferdinando, had resolutely evaded the tax on a piece of land he owned adjacent to the Garden of Remembrance. Don Antonio had his eye on this land and Don Ferdinando had evaded no less resolutely all attempts on the part of Don Antonio to get him to part with it. A reckoning was due, but the gypsies were devils.

Manolo came stuttering up behind Don Antonio on his motor scooter. He stopped just past the Mayor, who swung himself immediately onto the saddle behind his agent. Manolo released the brake and the machine jumped forward.

"How is it going?" shouted Don Antonio.

"Well, very well," said Manolo, as usual.

"Franco is coming on the eighth."

"Franco!" Manolo wrung his hand and looked back, looked forward again to swerve past a donkey as it advanced, apparently sightless, into the *carretera*. "Gypsy!"

"Can we be ready?"

"Ready?"

"To receive him at The Cock?"

"Today's the seventeenth!"

"We must be," shouted Don Antonio. "All we need is the terrace, the bar and the downstairs lavatories, in case——"

"It might be done."

"It must be done."

Manolo jigged the scooter in under one of the plane trees at the front of the café site and pulled up.

"You go on." The Mayor dismounted. "I must see Pepe."

While Manolo went on his pointed toes up the steps to the platform of the terrace, Don Antonio returned a few yards down the road until he came to the entrance of the Garden of Remembrance. The Garden ran parallel to the *carretera* for a space of seventy-five meters. It was thirty meters deep. A gravel path ran the length of it, set with benches at regular intervals. A second short path bisected the other at right angles. At the point of intersection was a small pool decked with goldfish. In the center was an earthenware mermaid, glazed green. She held the spout of a narrow water jet between her breasts. The force of the jet could be regulated by a tap set in the ground at the side of the pool just under the plaque which informed those who enjoyed the Garden that it had been planted in memory of Doña Pilar, Don Antonio's wife, who had died in 1951, aged thirty-six.

Pepe the gardener stood with one hand in the pocket of his blue cotton trousers, a yellow cigarette in his lips and the ear-flaps of his leather cap popped together on the top of his head. His thumb was over the nozzle of a hose. He moved his wrist and the fan of water spread casually over the dry bed.

"Good morning, Pepe."

"Don Antonio." Pepe removed the cigarette from his mouth and squashed it against his thumbnail before putting it behind his ear.

"Everything all right?"

"Gypsy children haven't been——"

"No, no."

"I gave that Ramón a clip he won't forget."

"You did."

"None of the children in this village appreciate what a garden like this means. They're better off throwing orange peel at each other. Well now, Pepe, I've got some news for you. The Caudillo is coming to Torreroja."

"I heard."

"Well, I'll tell you something you haven't heard. He's going to come directly through here, through the Garden of Remembrance. Along this very path. With his staff. What do you say to that?"

Pepe wrinkled his brows and switched the arc of water to another bed.

"After refreshments, the Head of State will pass along this very path, through the arches you will be putting up and so eventually to the cars which will be drawn up, down there, to receive him."

Pepe's eyebrows jumped up and descended.

"You can see how much depends on you, my friend. I want Torreroja to have the best decorations in the entire province. I have decided on solid wooden arches plaited with palm and cane, with laurel wreaths at appropriate places and a large silver slogan across the top of each: 'Wecome to Our Savior'."

"Savior? To me——"

"He saved us from Communism," said Don Antonio. "In any case, I shall be speaking personally to Placido about the lettering. There's no call for you to concern yourself with it. I happen to know where you and I would have been if the Reds had won. Up against a wall. Believe me, I know. One doesn't argue with a father, two sisters and four brothers. I want three arches. One, two and three, so. All right?"

"Very well."

"And then there's the mosaic."

"Mosaic?"

"To commemorate the visit. I've already ordered it from José Lerida. I haven't been idle, I can promise you that. Yes, the mosaic's to go—come with me, man, come with me—here, directly in front of the fountain. José will show you what to do. You can count on its being one meter square. Exactly."

On the terrace of The Cock, Don Leonardo, the local captain of the Civil Guard, was waiting for the Mayor. He was fingering the bulbous brown mole which grew in the center of his thin black mustache. A heavy man, bulging from the narrow café chair, he had exceptionally large ears with pendant lobes. He came from Bilbao.

"I am sorry to be late," said the Mayor, looking round for his coffee, "but you can't get them to do anything around here without having to push them, push them all the time." He clapped his hands. "Come along, come along."

Don Leonardo rotated his lacquered hat, which lay on the table in front of him.

"If it weren't for people like you and me," said Antonio, "nothing would ever be done around here." He took a wad of papers from his pocket. "Well, we've got a few things to discuss, eh?" First of all, Don Antonio proposed that all shops be shut from lunch time, so that no one might have the excuse of business to prevent them from paying their respects to the Head of State. Strong pressure was to be put on the owners of shops and cafés along the *carretera* to make them spend lavishly on flags and decorations. Further, the Mayor intended to have all the curbstones whitened and patriotic slogans written in the roadway. All school children would have a holiday. To none of these proposals did Don Leonardo offer the smallest criticism. From time to time he tugged at the lobe of his ear, that was all. Don Antonio, however, argued each of his suggestions with a full range of reasons. There would be nothing of which the Captain had not heard. "I assume," said Don Antonio, reaching the actual day itself, "that there will be no question of a siesta for the police or the Guardia?"

The Captain rotated his hat.

"The Caudillo arrives at four forty-five. Well, we shall certainly need maximum security for the entire day up until that time, don't you agree? Otherwise one never knows who might sneak into town, conceal himself and then, when the time comes make some sort of disturbance. We shall have to keep our eyes open for anyone who looks as though he might—López, for instance."

"López?"

"The carpenter. I'm told he's an anarchist. He reads books published abroad."

Don Leonardo picked up his hat and inspected the red silk

lining.

"He wishes to emigrate to Australia," said Don Leonardo.

"Precisely. Well, you've thought of all this, of course; I merely raise the point so that you know where I stand."

The Captain nodded and eased his trousers. He was ready to put his hat on, but Don Antonio was not finished yet. He had still to secure the Captain's agreement to the notion that to complete the terrace where Torreroja was to entertain the Caudillo was a matter of public interest and should be paid for from public funds. To this, cosseted by his favorite *seco*, Don Leonardo made no objection. He could scarcely see how the issue fell within his sphere. Nevertheless, Don Antonio argued his case forcefully and in full.

By the time the two men left The Cock, it was twenty minutes past two. Don Antonio marched through the roasting village. The clip of his malacca cane announced him to the tenants of the houses along his road. His own street lay deep in sunshine up to the eaves of the houses. He had hoped it would be empty, but it was not: she was waiting for him again. Her feet crabbed pebbles from the burning bed of the roadway. She was not waiting, he told himself. She was simply still there. In fact, she ignored him until he was practically at his door, then she looked up and showed her broken teeth. The Mayor could see a stroke of fresh blood on her cracked lower lip. He tapped on his front door with his cane.

The girl squatted suddenly in the road and lifted her skirt up to her waist. The Mayor banged for Carmela. The girl was squatting down right in front of his own house. Look at her, and he couldn't help seeing the clump of hair on her groin. He thumped again with his cane. "Come along."

The door opened.

"Look at her. Look at her. You've got to do something about her. She can't stay around here all day. Look at her."

"What?"

"She——" The girl was standing several yards down the road. Her back was to the Mayor and she was crabbing stones with her feet. "She was squatting down there a moment ago like an animal. Like an animal! She's too old to piss in the road like a two-year-old. I know what she is, but she's too old all the same. It's an insult to public morals. She's got to be trained. She can't go on pissing in the road and that's all there is to it."

"Where did she?"

Don Antonio strode to the place where the girl had been. "But I saw her," he said. "I saw her, right here, she——"

Carmela was inspecting the dry place.

"Yes?"

"She lifted her skirt, she squatted down—I saw her with my own eyes. Well, what else did she do it for if not——? You've got to do something about her, send her away. She mustn't be allowed around here."

"Where can I send her?"

"I don't know. She can't stay around here."

"No."

"You say no, but what happens? She sits outside my front door all day. What kind of an impression does it make when people come to see the Mayor and find an idiot? She can't come here. If you can't arrange something, you'll—— Why can't your sister look after her?"

"She's working now. They can't fish. She has to go out to work. There's no one in the house."

"She can still stay there."

"She won't. She goes out."

"Tie her up. I don't know—but something has to be done. It——" Don Antonio pointed to the dry road "—it can't be permitted, that's all." He barged through the front door of his house. "She can't be allowed."

"Antonio, is that you?"

"Yes, Mother, yes."

Don Antonio slotted his cane in the umbrella stand and continued into the patio, where his lunch was laid. His son was at one end of the blue wooden table, eating grapes from a fat bunch.

"Something wrong, Father?"

"That girl, did she disturb you this morning?"

"Not really." Francisco put both elbows on the table and bent his neck to get at more grapes.

Don Antonio clapped his hands. "Either she disturbed you or she did not disturb you. What were you doing this morning?" He waited until some grape pips were worked to the front of his son's mouth and ejected. "You put too much in at the same time. If you eat too much, you'll get fat. If you get fat, you can't work. When is my lunch coming?"

"Now, immediately, Don Antonio."

"You have not told me what you were doing this morning."

"Oh, a lot of things. We talked about America."

"What about America?"

"The life of the people. It's very different from here. For instance, the young people, people of my age——"

"Why were you discussing this? In what subject?"

"English."

"You spoke in English of this, the life of the young people?"

"Yes, Father. She's been doing her mess in the street again, hasn't she?"

"Never mind. She should never come around here," said Don Antonio loudly, as Carmela came in from the kitchen with a plate of *boquerones* fried in yellow batter. "She has a bad effect on everyone."

Francisco slid off his chair.

"Where are you going?"

"To work. The American set me some sums to do."

"Excellent. You must learn to cope with figures. It's very important. You go and work. No one will bother you, I'll make sure of that. Come here a moment."

"Father?"

Don Antonio pulled out his handkerchief. There were scabs of grapeskin clinging to the phantom mustache above his son's mouth. "Always keep your face clean. Your mother wouldn't like you not to be clean. Always keep yourself clean for her sake."

"Yes, Father. Father——"

"Yes, my son."

"Is it true that in America she wouldn't be as she is?"

"She? Who? Oh—what, you mean——? Of course not. What's wrong with her comes from God. No one could do anything about her except Him."

"She couldn't have been cured in America?"

"No. I told you. No."

"Not if——"

"Francisco, if you have work to do, go and do it."

Carmela was standing in the kitchen door.

"Go along."

The boy went, his legs fat in his short trousers.

Don Antonio pushed his plate from him. Carmela came away from the doorpost and removed the plate. She returned with some fried liver and a dish of shredded lettuce on which stood two tomatoes so sliced that they fell open in two red flowers.

"Don Antonio——"

"Already?"

"May I speak to you?"

"Now what is it?" demanded her employer, as though he had dealt with one request and was now faced with another. "Well?"

"Don Antonio, you told me that when the new café was finished——"

"It's not finished. Please don't bother me until it is."

"It will be by the time Franco comes, won't it?"

"Who told you about Franco?"

"They told me in the market."

"No one knows how to do anything in this town except gossip." Don Antonio helped himself to salad.

"I still owe money to the doctor. You said that when the café was completed I could work in the kitchen, as cook. Now they say a cook is coming from Málaga; they say——"

"You listen to too much gossip. Nothing is settled yet."

"It's the money, Don Antonio. I still owe the doctor."

"Do what your sister did when she owed León money. This liver is tough. It's leather. You and Paco——It's overcooked as well."

"You told me two o'clock. Don Antonio, you did say that I could earn more money when the café opened; you said——"

"Do you think I don't know what I said? You dare to stand there and tell me—serve food like this—you ruin my lunch and then you——" Don Antonio tossed his plate across the patio. "Get it out of here and that daughter of yours as well. Clear it up and stop sniffling and get out." He pushed back his chair and went indoors.

"Is that you, Antonio?"

"Yes, Mother, yes."

"She's insolent, that woman, insolent."

"Yes, Mother." Don Antonio went into his office.

The rocking chair squeaked and creaked, squeaked and creaked.

In the patio, Carmela was picking up the slices of broken earthenware. The ends of Don Antonio's liver she placed carefully on the largest section.

Don Antonio did not sleep during the siesta hour. He worked. Sitting forward on his swivel chair, he listened to the silence of Torreroja and knew that in every instant of it he was drawing ahead of those who affected to compete with him. The sun forced Torreroja to close its eyes, but the Mayor, mantled in the thick shadows of his study, was determined to keep his wide open. He lifted his head from his correspondence and listened. Somewhere was the rustle of whispering voices. He capped his Parker and left the room.

"What's she doing here?"

Carmela's arm grabbed the side of her chair.

"How many people do I feed in this house?" Don Antonio wrenched the plate from under the girl's nose. "What's this? No wonder I had tough liver. *She* gets the tender pieces. An idiot gets the master portion!"

"It's what you threw on the floor."

"Liar! Woman, you're a liar."

"It's what I took from the floor. She hasn't had meat in ten days."

"I've told you before. I will not have my house used as a lunatic asylum. Now get her out of here, at once."

The girl smiled and took the last of the liver and put it in her mouth.

"She's not to come here. She'll shit in the hall—there's no knowing what she'll do. My son lives here. If his mother knew that a girl like that was coming in and out of the house——"

"If you'd given me the money for the doctor, Don Antonio,

she would not be as she is."

The idiot laughed in his face.

"That's a lie. Now get her out of here."

"The doctor himself told me when she was first ill that if I could get the money——"

"Why didn't you go to him on your back?" shouted Don Antonio. "Like your sister did? She managed. You could have got the drugs if you'd really wanted to."

"He needed money himself, to buy them."

"He's got plenty of money. All doctors are cheats. He's not short. I've paid him enough in my time. Anyway, I gave you some money myself——"

"A hundred pesetas! I needed five thousand."

"Five thousand! I need five hundred thousand, does that mean someone's going to give it to me? Five thousand pesetas for this?" He raised the girl by her shoulder and dragged her from the table with a piece of bread in her hand. "Do you think I'm going to bail out every idiot in Spain at five thousand pesetas a time? I don't ever want to see her in this house again."

"She has to eat."

"She doesn't have to eat here." Don Antonio stopped at the door to turn on Carmela. "And you want to work at The Cock! How many people are you intending to give free meals to *then*, eh?" He yanked the girl through the house. She smiled at him with blood-caked lips. "You go out of here and you don't come back." She smiled.

"Father, what's happening?"

"Nothing, where have you been? I thought you were going to work."

"I went for some chocolate, that's all." Francisco stared at the girl as she went close by him on her way to the street. She grinned at him and made claws.

"Francisco, you'd better go upstairs now and get down to that work of yours."

Carmela was sobbing in the kitchen.

"Women!" Don Antonio pitched the girl into the heat and banged the front door so that the knocker rapped independently, like a ghost.

"Antonio, is that you?"

"Yes, Mother, yes." He went into his study and banged that door too.

The rocking chair creaked and squeaked.

There was a knock on the study door.

"Now what?" Don Antonio swiveled his chair to the door.

"I'm going to my house." Carmela had a basket over her arm and a scarf round her head. Her black dress was closed over her throat.

"You're leaving, yes?"

"I'm going to my house."

"Then go." Don Antonio swiveled back to bend over his work. "Why don't you?" He picked up his pen. "What are you waiting for?"

"My money."

"Money? Haven't I been feeding your entire family?"

"My money, Don Antonio, and then I go to my house."

"Go back in the kitchen and finish your work and stop bothering me and we'll say no more about it. It's forgotten."

"My money, Don Antonio."

"Do you ever think that I might have better things to worry about than you? Do you realize that this whole town depends on me?" Don Antonio leaned forward. "Just who do you think you're going to work for if you leave here? Who's going to employ you?"

"Foreigners. They pay better and you work less."

"Foreigners! You leave this house, you leave this village. You leave the province. You go to prison if necessary." Don Antonio went to shut the door of the study. He held his wrists vertical. "With handcuffs on, you understand? I know you're a thief. Don't think I don't. You're all thieves. I know. You work in this house or you don't work at all. Finish."

"You promised me work in the café——"

"I want young girls in the café, sixteen, seventeen——"

"But to *cook*, Don Antonio."

"What do you know about restaurant catering? Nothing. You fry a bit of fish——"

"I'm the best cook in Torreroja."

"And you work here."

"Don Antonio, the doctor——Don Antonio, I've cooked for twenty or thirty people in this house. I can cook for as many as you want. Any number."

"I'm having proper professionals. I want the best restaurant on the coast. I'm not handing out a few pieces of fried fish."

"I'm going to my house."

He grabbed her. "You have no house. Your sister rents a house, that's all. I can have you all turned out if necessary. They owe rent."

"My brother-in-law can't fish."

"Exactly. They owe rent. You can be turned out whenever I say so and you won't find a house between here and Madrid."

"Very well."

"You'll be in the street."

"Very well."

"You're mad. You're mad. All of you." He shoved Carmela's shoulder. She let go of the neck of her dress and backed away. "Mad." He pushed her and she fell back, slowly, onto the low leather-covered chaise lounge under the shuttered window. The springs grated. "I want you to understand for once and for all, no one goes out of this house."

Her eyes held a strange humor. She raised an eyebrow. Don Antonio bent down and gripped her shoulders. She tipped backwards and her bosom rode up in her dress. The springs of the rusty chaise longue grated and ground.

"I don't like people to threaten that they are leaving," said Don Antonio at last.

"And you built her a garden," said Carmela, pulling her dress under her hips and making the springs grate once more.

"What are you talking about?"

"Accident," said Carmela. "Ha!"

"Get on now. And I don't want any more nonsense."

"I don't want your money."

"Take it. Take it, when I tell you."

"Garden of Remembrance."

"Go on. And I don't want to hear any more about the doctor."

"Ha!" She closed her black dress over her throat.

Don Antonio pulled the woman back into the room and opened the neck of her dress and put his hand in on her breast. She stared at him. He took the nipple between his finger and thumb and smiled. "Now go on."

Francisco was sitting on the third step of the stairs. Carmela passed him without a word and went into the kitchen. Francisco was carving a piece of cane into a flute with his penknife. Carmela sat down at the kitchen table, hunched her shoulders over her plate and went on with her meal. She finished by wiping her bread round the plate and then drank a cup of water although there were glasses.

Don Antonio was in the washroom which opened off his study. He always used potassium permanganate.

The rocker creaked in the dark front room. There was the chink of a rosary and a muttering of names as if in a litany: "Jaime, María, Pepe, Sandro, José . . ."

The day before the Caudillo was due in Torreroja, the Military Governor drove out from Málaga in his black Seat. Don Antonio and Don Leonardo met him at the Municipal Center. After coffee, they joined him in his car for a tour of the route, after which the car returned to The Cock.

"Such are our modest preparations, Your Excellency."

"We shall now rehearse the actual arrival of the Caudillo," said the Military Governor to his aide. "For the purposes of the rehearsal, I shall impersonate the Head of State."

"His Excellency wishes to rehearse your arrangements for the actual arrival of the Head of State. For this purpose, he himself will impersonate the Head of State."

"What a good idea, Your Excellency!"

The Military Governor pursed his lips. His sunglasses were quite opaque. He had already had a full rehearsal in Málaga and he had inspected all the little villages between that city and Torreroja. The idea was hardly fresh to him.

Don Antonio and Don Leonardo waited on the terrace of The Cock. The Military Governor's Seat vanished round the corner past the red brick castle which gave Torreroja its name and reappeared moving at high speed. It drew up in front of The Cock,

from which the two local officials descended to meet it. As they
emerged, the Military Governor whispered to his aide. "The
Military Governor thinks you should not *descend* to the Caudillo," the aide said to Don Antonio.

"Of course not, Your Excellency, of course not. If Your Excellency would care to——" Don Antonio indicated the steps
with his hand. "I believe I am right in thinking that my father,
the late Colonel Francis Xavier de Córdoba y Albeñiz, once had
the honor of accompanying Your Excellency, who was then——"

The Military Governor made some comment to his aide.

"His Excellency has no idea what you're talking about. He
thinks you must be mistaken."

"I understood," said Don Antonio, "that His Excellency was
impersonating the Head of State. It was to him that I intended——"

The Military Governor spoke to his aide.

"There is no need, His Excellency says, for you to repeat to
him every word you intend for the Caudillo. He is concerned
with security, not with elocution."

"As His Excellency wishes," said Don Antonio. "Now, if you
would care to step inside——"

All was complete. The coffee machine was in place. The bottles were ranged in rows. The stools were at the bar. The restaurant tables wore starched skirts and bore gleaming glasses. A
special counter was being installed in the main reception room
where delicacies expressly ordered from Málaga would be avail-
able for the distinguished guests. Don Antonio snapped his fingers for Manolo to join them. "If there is anything Your Excellency thinks we should do further, my assistant——"

The Military Governor looked round. "It seems suitable
enough. The Caudillo doesn't like a great deal of show."

"No, no, of course. Well, we're only a modest village——"

The Military Governor spoke to his aide.

"His Excellency wishes to know if this café belongs to you."

"Yes, Your Excellency, to myself and to some associates of
mine. But of course on an occasion like this, it is nothing more
nor less than Torreroja's. In fact, so far as my own personal
pocket is concerned——"

The Military Governor wanted to know something else.

"His Excellency is concerned to be told why the reception is not to be held at the Municipal Center."

"Don Leonardo and I," said Don Antonio with a quick look at the Captain, "discussed this at great length and we came to the conclusion that the Caudillo could be more suitably entertained here. The Municipal Center is somewhat airless and rather—austere. We hoped the Caudillo would care for the best that Torreroja's present-day craftsmen are capable of. However, if Your Excellency is of the opinion——"

"His Excellency doesn't consider it of any importance. He was merely curious. He would like to know who these girls are."

"Yes, of course; well first of all, they're all local girls——"

"Why are they dressed as they are?" said the aide.

"They're waitresses," said Don Antonio.

"His Excellency thinks they should wear shawls. They're not modest."

"Shawls for the girls," said Don Antonio to Manolo.

The Military Governor was looking through the glass doors which gave onto the swimming pool. He whispered to his aide.

"His Excellency is concerned that no one be swimming in the pool when the Caudillo arrives."

"No one is to swim in the pool," said Don Antonio to Manolo.

Don Antonio led the way to the back of the café. The new lavatory seats were in place. Each was wrapped in virgin cellophane until the coming of the Caudillo.

"Now if Your Excellency would come this way——"

They went down the steps to the entrance of the Garden of Remembrance. The Military Governor spoke to his aide. The aide spoke to Don Leonardo, who nodded.

"Is something wrong?"

"A question of security," said Don Leonardo.

The triumphal arches were in place (Don Antonio glanced sideways at the Military Governor to see his reaction, but the sunglasses gave nothing away); the full effect would not, of course, be seen until the greenery was added. This would have to be done at the last moment; otherwise it would certainly sadden. On the other hand, the mosaic was done; its chips of blue, gold, silver and red sparkled like a fractured rainbow. On every side, flowers echoed its brilliance. The Military Governor spoke to his aide and the aide addressed Don Leonardo.

"What does His Excellency think?"

"A question of security."

The Military Governor had a new question.

"His Excellency wishes to know why it is necessary for the Caudillo to walk through here at all."

"The Garden is, I think, the pride of Torreroja. In addition, it is well known that the Head of State is much attached to flowers. Some of the blooms here—— Well, and apart from that, after many miles in a motor car it's sometimes pleasant to stretch one's legs——"

The Military Governor whispered to his aide.

"What does His Excellency——?"

"A question of security."

"Of course," said Don Antonio as they went to the car, "these are only the modest arrangements of a poor village——"

"His Excellency is satisfied. You should all be in your places by half past three at the latest. There is no certainty about the hour of the Caudillo's arrival. You will be informed of any developments which may occur."

As the car drove off, Don Leonardo came to the salute.

"He approved," said Don Antonio.

Don Leonardo came down from the salute to scratch the lobe of his ear. "Good. Now——" It was time for a drink.

The day of the Caudillo's coming was one of exceptional heat. The women whitening the curbstones dripped sweat into the buckets of whitewash. Don Antonio told Pepe to be ready to hose down the triumphal arches so that they might appear fresh and green. Not only was Franco's name displayed on walls and in windows, but Don Antonio had a gang at work inscribing his name, in huge capital letters, in the very roadway along which he was to pass.

"Antonio, is that you?"

"Yes, Mother." Don Antonio walked into his mother's room. "Today is the day when Franco comes to Torreroja, Mother."

"You have told me so."

"And I shall receive him in the name of the village."

"I saw him once," said Doña Elisabeta, "in nineteen hundred and thirty-four, in the Asturian War. He was like a fighting cock. He saved Spain."

"Yes, Mother." He heard the clink of the rosary in Doña Elisabeta's hand.

"He was riding in an open car and later your father sat next to him at dinner in the mess." The voice weakened; she was telling the beads. "Jaime, José, María, Sandro . . ."

The knocker clumped on the front door. Don Antonio heard the scuffing of Carmela's slippers. She was holding the neck of her black dress across her throat as she passed Don Antonio.

"Good morning, Carmela."

Don Antonio said: "Mr. Stern, I was not expecting you to come today."

"I was not sure," said Adam Stern.

"Today is a holiday for all the children. My son does not work today. Today is sacred to Spain."

"I understand."

"It is a day no foreigner can truly understand. Today we honor God and Spain. And today my son will see the face which saved Spain for God."

"I understand, Don Antonio."

"Today carries a lesson, my friend, more important than any he could learn elsewhere, even from a man with three degrees from American universities."

"Of course."

"Today my son will come face to face with the destiny of Spain. No one in a thousand hours of school could instruct him in what he will learn in a few minutes this afternoon."

"Of course."

"In Spain we care, above all, for the ideal. The Spaniard gives himself for nothing else. Nothing in American life compares with this. Francisco has been out since early morning. He is setting an example for the rest of the children. His mother would have been proud of him. By the way, I would advise you to be in your place early, Mr. Stern. Four forty-five exactly, he arrives."

"Thank you, Don Antonio. Until tomorrow then."

"Until tomorrow, Mr. Stern."

When Don Antonio left the house, the street was already brimming with people in their best clothes. Several of the local children were making designs in the dust on a foreigner's car. One was teasing air from the valve on one of the front tires. The children scattered, chirruping when they saw Don Antonio.

"I hope," he said, leaning on his cane, "that you will all be washing your hands and faces before the Caudillo arrives. My son is already in his place, waiting."

They ran about.

Even the gypsies, sitting at their café, were dressed in style. Their women were standing around, their breasts jutting out into the pavement, all made up and with flowers in their hair. Of their King, however, Don Ferdinando, there was no sign.

"Good morning, Don Antonio," they called. "Good morning."

"Good morning, good morning," said Don Antonio.

The women smiled and looked under their sooty lashes as he went through them. Their brothers, with slicked hair, watched. Don Antonio made a big chest. Everywhere his plans were being carried out to the letter. The village had burst into flower, color in every corner. Above all, The Cock was supreme. The tower had reached its peak. Strings of colored lights—for there was to be a Gala Opening Ball that night to cap the celebrations—hung across the terrace and over the entrance. From the spire of the tower yards of bunting were draped to each corner of the café. Even those who had been known to ignore Don Antonio went out of their way to congratulate him. He shook over a hundred hands between the Plaza and The Cock. No one felt himself able to afford losing the chance of a smile, the touch of his hand. The Mayor was the town. The only faces which paid him no homage were those of some of the special Guardias drafted to Torreroja on security duty. They knew nothing of the village or of its aristocracy. Their faces were unsmiling. Their boots paced out the dusty road.

The Garden of Remembrance was also lined with flags. The silver lettering on the arches glittered in the sun. When Don Antonio passed through on his eleventh or twelfth journey of inspection, he could almost fancy that it was for himself that this dazzling welcome was spelt out.

"Don Antonio, if you could spare me one moment——" It was the carpenter, López, who was concerned with the temporary building which was to provide shade for Don Antonio and the rest of the reception committee down at the roadside. "If you could possibly come and approve of what we have done, Don Antonio."

"Of course."

Someone rode up on a motorcycle. "Don Antonio——"

"One moment." The Mayor shook the frame of the sun shelter. It seemed firm. He nodded and ran his finger along the planing.

"Some sandpaper here."

"Yes, Don Antonio. At once." López bowed. López bowed!

The morning passed. The sun reached its zenith. All was ready. The Mayor looked up and down the *carretera,* which, in the full heat, lay puddled with mirages. Only the Guardias were to be seen. Don Antonio went slowly up the steps of the terrace. He went through into the washroom and put his face under the tap. He wiped it on his handkerchief. He did not care to touch the clean white towels nor to pass water in the virgin bowls with their cellophane seats. He went down to Don Ferdinando's field and relieved himself there. The gypsies always used it. Returning, he went into the Garden of Remembrance. The triumphal arches were dull with dust again. The gravel could do with a rake. He called Pepe, who rose from a pad of shade under an orange tree.

Half past four, the sun was hanging like a tilted bucket of molten metal in a sky which showed no shred of a cloud. The mountains behind Torreroja were ribbed with shadow, but elsewhere there was no suggestion of evening. Nor was there any indication of the Caudillo's coming. The road carried its usual traffic of lorries and cars. Each one that rolled impudently over the lettering which spelt FRANCO on the tarmac received a furious scowl from Don Antonio when it drew level with the café. Luckily, however, the day was so dry that no mark was left on the whitewash.

Don Antonio, his best suit buttoned, his shoes glassy, his tie tight under his red throat, waited by the roadside. He peered along towards the village. There were not enough people. He sent Manolo to the head of the Municipal Police: the people must be encouraged to line the route. A quarter to five was almost upon them. He could come at any moment.

A black Seat emerged from behind the castle. Don Antonio's toes contracted against his hot soles. People were crowding to the curbs. Don Antonio recognized a pair of sunglasses in the back of the car. The Military Governor was making his last tour. Don Antonio went forward.

"Good afternoon, Your Excellency."

"His Excellency wishes me to tell you that there has been an unavoidable delay. The Caudillo will not be here for one hour."

The car went away on its new tires.

Don Antonio called for lemonade. The heat seemed to be growing. Only the Garden of Remembrance looked lush and cool.

"There ought to be more people," said Don Antonio. "Round here, I mean. After all, this is where he's going to stop."

Actually, he had noticed, the alien Guardias were giving discouraging looks to those citizens who were making their way up to The Cock. They did not seem to appreciate the importance of a packed welcome for the Caudillo. What mattered to them was that there should be no trouble.

To Don Antonio's relief, the gypsies began to come across from their café. Though he despised them for the animals they were, he resented them for their independence and he feared their powers. Now if they were coming, it was because they knew —he didn't ask how—that Franco was on his way.

"Where's Don Ferdinando?" the Mayor asked Manolo.

Manolo shrugged.

"He ought to be here. Insolent old——"

"He'll come, when it suits him."

"He should be made to come."

Manolo shrugged. "Yes."

"Have you seen my son?"

"This morning."

"I thought he would come here. Well, at least the crowd's

getting bigger."

"Of course."

The gypsies had gathered in a tight crowd now, their backs to everyone.

"What're they talking about?"

"Who knows?"

"They mustn't turn their backs."

"They won't, when the time comes."

A couple of Guardias were standing near the gypsy circle. The slim gypsy boys inspected them. They actually turned round and inspected them.

"Don Ferdinando should keep them in order."

"He's the biggest rogue of all."

"Don't tell me."

Don Leonardo was scratching the lobe of his ear.

"See if you can find Francisco," said Don Antonio to Manolo.

It was all but six o'clock. The edges of the sky were badged with gold. Manolo came back. There was no sign of Francisco. "No matter," said Don Antonio. "Do the girls have their shawls?"

"Taken care of."

"Find me some more lemonade."

Suddenly faces were falling forward over the road like blooms snapped off by the slash of a cane. A motorcyclist was whipping down the hill from the castle. He braked sharply, scalding dust from the road, and drew up by the Mayor. "Ten minutes," he announced and was gone on double exhausts.

The word was passed through the people.

Don Leonardo was talking to an officer of the Guardia.

Don Antonio took the lemonade from Manolo and drank it quickly, eyes right over the glass along the road. "That's better. Now, is everything all right?"

"Yes, yes."

"Make sure. We've got just eight minutes before——"

Half an hour later, a subdued droning could be heard some-where behind the castle. It rose and rose in power and pitch un-til it seemed to fill the whole sky. And then, from round the cor-ner of the castle—even the gypsies were staring—came three, six,

nine, twelve, fifteen motorcycle troopers in black leather uniforms with white crash helmets, white crossed shoulder straps
and black sten guns. They wore huge goggles. The buzz changed
to a drumming roar. Three, six, nine, twelve, fifteen, they were
through the village. They were gone. Don Leonardo scratched the
red lobe of his ear. The road was empty. Fully ten minutes passed
before people spoke above a whisper.

Now there were Guardias everywhere; they came from the al-
leyways, down from the castle, machine guns ready. Don Antonio
reviewed them uneasily. Don Leonardo nodded to the Guardia
officer, whose men began to push first the gypsies and then the
other people back from the road. Don Antonio watched the gypsies anxiously; if they abandoned the proceedings, he was afraid
it would be unlucky. The Guardias continued with their work.
They bullied the gypsies back until the last of them all but fell
into the beds of the Garden of Remembrance. "Keep them out
of there," shouted Don Antonio. "Not in there."

The droning came again. It rose and rose in power and pitch
and then—three, six, nine, twelve, fifteen, eighteen, twenty-one
—twenty-one motorcyclists darted into view, bore down on the
village and were gone. The attention of the people was fastened
on the road. They were bereft of speech. Only the Guardias at-
tended to their business and not to the road. They craned their
heads in among the shrubbery of the Garden of Remembrance.
Don Antonio controlled his fury as, under the instructions of
their alien officer, they even stepped among the beds and peered
behind the triumphal arches. They kept jostling the gypsies until one of the latter suddenly shot out his arm and pointed with
his finger, one of those skinny, double-jointed fingers, bent back
with its own rigidity.

A single slim figure was ambling along the road. Right down
the center of the *carretera* came Don Ferdinando, his horn-
handled cane hung on a leather loop over his wrist, a snappy
trilby at an angle on his head, white-and-black shoes on his feet
and his dancer's body sheathed in a lightweight gray cotton suit.
Round his waist was a red sash and in his buttonhole a red car-
nation. In his mouth he had a long bamboo cigarette holder with
a king-sized cigarette in it. He walked down the center of the

road until he came to the stenciled lettering FRANCO. He stepped with elegant precision into the hollow triangle of the A, paused, made out the name of the Caudillo for himself and with a smile of radiant majesty proceeded towards Don Antonio.

The Guardias looked at their officer and their officer looked at Don Leonardo. There was much blinking and looking at boots. The gypsies' faces were slashed with white smiles. The people, one or two of them, clapped. Don Ferdinando strolled —how could a man take such long strides and still cover the ground with such slowness?—directly up to Don Antonio and put out his hand.

"Not late, I hope?"

Don Antonio clenched his fists. His teeth ground together. "Arrest him," he said to Don Leonardo, "arrest him before— before, before we have—— Get him away from here."

One of the gypsies shouted something. Don Antonio could not understand. They were all traitors, that was certain. They were laughing, the girls were swinging their skirts and pivoting about.

"Get them away from here."

Don Leonardo spoke to the alien officer. The officer waved to his men, who waded into the gypsies. Two came for Don Ferdinando. He brought up his cane. "One moment! One moment!" He twitched the cane. "One moment! I come to reveal something—an ambush!"

"He's a crazy gypsy. Get him away from here. Get him away."

"There are people hidden. Concealed." Don Ferdinando pointed with the tip of his cane at the Garden of Remembrance. "There!"

"Get him away. He's a madman. He's crazy."

Don Leonardo scratched the lobe of his ear. "Better have a look," he said to the alien officer. "Be quick."

Don Antonio, looking at his watch, said: "Stay where you are, everyone. Stay where you are."

But they were all surging towards the place which Don Ferdinando had indicated. The King was there among his subjects now, smiling and shaking hands.

"If there's no one there, he should be arrested."

The Guardias were trampling the garden.

"There's nothing there. They'll——"

A sudden thrashing rose in the middle of the green. Like game disturbed by a dog, something was flapping and snapping among the foliage. Don Ferdinando put his eyebrows together and looked most offendedly at Don Antonio. Don Leonardo unhitched the flap of his revolver holster. Don Antonio wanted a cigar, a glass of lemonade, a gun. Don Ferdinando spread his arms and the people laughed and cheered.

From a clump of green Guardias, the naked, flat-chested body of a girl reared up, like a stripped bird, and for an interminable second, Don Antonio saw a badge of hair and two scraggy legs before the wild, fluttering creature was borne away through the back of the garden towards Don Ferdinando's field. The boy's olive face was sullen, not demonic. His hands were at his front. He went the same way with no suggestion of flight.

A whistle blew. The first car was descending from the castle, which, as the sun dropped, burned scarlet in the evening sky.

"They're coming!"

Another car was behind the first, another behind that. A sequence of wide black limousines streamed out from behind the red castle. The first one passed over FRANCO in the road. The second car was over it now and the first was almost up to The Cock. Don Antonio stared into the road. He could scarcely face the Caudillo. The first black car, unwinding a siren like a streamer behind it, rolled past where Don Antonio and Don Leonardo were waiting. Which car contained the Caudillo? No one had said. The second car went past. The first car was all but through the village. The fourth car was over FRANCO. The eighth car came from behind the castle. The third car was past Don Antonio. The first car was on the road to Málaga. The eleventh car was in sight from behind the castle. The sixth was over FRANCO. In which packed car was the Caudillo? Who knew? The Guardias were rigid at the salute. Don Leonardo was stiff. Don Ferdinando had his hat on his breast. The third car was through the village. The ninth was over FRANCO. Generals, admirals, security men, black car after black car, each ribbed with chrome, distinguished with ministerial number plates of the highest priority, all went through. The fifth car had quit the village. The nineteenth was out from behind the castle. The fourteenth was over FRANCO. The dust burned in Don Antonio's eyes. The nineteenth car was over FRANCO. The nineteenth car was through the village. The nineteenth car was on the road to Málaga. One last motorcyclist buzzed out from behind the castle and flitted through the village.

For a minute, the people awaited a miracle. Then the smiles and the giggles began. Among the grinning faces, the Guardias were stern. The one nearest Don Antonio was whispering to himself: "With my own eyes, with my own eyes I saw him. In the fifth car. I saw him with my own eyes."

"I too," said his colleague. "In the second car."

"The Caudillo?" said a third. "He was leading, of course, in the very first car. I saw him myself, with my own eyes."

Don Antonio rubbed his thumb along his jaw. He looked round for Manolo. "Switch on the lights," he said. He walked along past the gypsies. They bowed. They deferred. They touched each other aside. The townspeople ignored him. They fell silent at his passing. He walked the long road to his house and opened his front door as furtively as a safebreaker.

"Antonio, is that you?"

"Yes, Mother, yes."

"It was a triumph, my son. Yes? I heard the cheering."

"Yes, Mother."

"And you, my son—you spoke to him?"

Don Antonio stood in the darkness with his mother and heard the clink of the rosary. "Yes, Mother," he said. "I spoke to him."

"And he remembered your father, the Colonel?"

"Yes, Mother."

"You spoke of their dining together in the mess at Burgos?"

"Of course, Mother. He asked me to bring you his profound greetings. I fancy he remembered you."

"Your father and he——"

"—were messmates. That was the word he used."

"They were Christian knights," said Doña Elisabeta. "You went with him through the Garden of Remembrance?"

"I did, Mother."

"Our dead are not lost. With such a man, our dead are not lost."

"No, Mother."

Don Antonio left the room.

"Jaime, Pia, José, Pepe . . ."

The rocker creaked, the rocker squeaked.

Don Antonio clamped shut the shutters of his office. He sat down on the rusty chaise longue. He sat there for an hour, perhaps longer. Then he went into the kitchen. Carmela was sitting at the table, hands folded in front of her, a shawl over her head.

"You've heard."

"I have," said the woman. "What do you want me to do? Do you want me to go?"

"No. If you leave this house, I will kill you."

"What do you want me to do?"

"Nothing."

"I understand."

"Take off your shawl."

"Yes."

"She must go from the village."

"Yes."

"I will pay whatever is necessary."

"Good."

"And the doctor. Whatever is necessary."

"Thank you."

"But you stay here."

"Yes."

"And no nonsense."

"I understand."

Don Antonio said: "The American will not be coming again. We shall be only ourselves."

"I understand."

Don Antonio went back to his office and sat down in his swivel chair. He leaned back. The thick spring at the back creaked as he put his weight against it.

"Fran-cis-co, Fran-cis-co, Fran-cis-co," the children were chanting in the street.

Don Antonio went to the window and opened the shutter an

inch, two inches. The children had gathered under the yellow street lamp. "Fran-cis-co, Fran-cis-co . . ." They were in a group by the front door, but Don Antonio could see no sign of his son.

In the hall he could hear their chanting "Fran-cis-co, Fran-cis-co, Fran-cis-co . . ." louder and more rhythmical. Don Antonio unsheathed his malacca cane from the umbrella stand.

"Francisco, Francisco, Francisco," they were calling faster.

Don Antonio threw back the lock and opened the door.

"FranciscoFranciscoFranciscoFranciscoFrancisco." The children were drubbing their fists in their palms. In the center of them, the spotted dog was busy with the bitch once more. "Francisco-FranciscoFrancisco! Olé!"

Don Antonio scattered them left and right with his fist. He raised his malacca cane and brought it down with his full force again across the back of the dog. There was a *crack-crack*, like two barrels of a gun going off. Then a yelp of agony stabbed out. The dog, laced into the bitch, was rolling and yapping and frothing. The shattered cane in Don Antonio's hand was like a bunch of reeds. Don Antonio's sharp shoes jabbed at the animal's belly and head. The dog slobbered and screamed and dragged itself, broken-backed, together with the bitch still, away from Don Antonio's anger. Don Antonio clawed after it and got to his knees and had his hands round its neck, safe from its drooling jaws, and so he strangled it. He tore the carcass out of the bitch. The bitch yelped and bit his hand. The teeth were in but an instant before Don Antonio snatched himself clear and kicked the beast down the road. He had the carcass of the dog. He took it, dangling by the neck, past the children and into his house. The door banged. The knocker clumped.

"Can you dispose of this?" said Don Antonio.

"A dog?"

"Yes."

"How——"

"It had an accident. I had to—finish it. It's not to leave here. I don't want it found by anyone."

"I can dig a grave in the patio."

"Now. Immediately."

"Very well."

"If the bitch whelps," muttered Don Antonio, "they must all be killed."

"I'll do it now," said Carmela, with a shovel.

She took the dog and went into the patio.

On his way back to the office, Don Antonio heard a tap at the front door.

"Antonio——"

"Yes, Mother, yes."

He opened the door.

It was Manolo.

"I'm sorry to disturb you, Don Antonio. But about the dance——"

"What of it?"

"Well, does it go on?"

"Of course it goes on. The Caudillo came. The café is finished. Of course it goes on."

"I thought perhaps——"

"How much did we say for the first drink?" There were faces at the street door. "Fifty pesetas the first drink?"

"Yes. Fifty."

"Make it a hundred," said Don Antonio.

"A hundred pesetas!"

"Yes," said Don Antonio. "If the people want to eat the refreshments prepared for the Caudillo, they must pay for them."

"A hundred pesetas, they'll never pay it."

"They'll pay it. You can tell them that I personally will take a hundred pesetas from everyone who comes to the dance tonight. I shall be there in person. To see it with my own eyes. You tell them."

"Yes, Don Antonio. Don Antonio, about the Caudillo——"

"There was a plot to kill him," said Don Antonio. "Some gypsies, I'm told. There've been some arrests already."

"Can I——?"

"Tell people? Certainly. The danger is past. Tonight we celebrate the Caudillo's escape. I shall expect everyone to be there. It's a question of loyalty."

"I understand, Don Antonio."

After Manolo had gone, Don Antonio went in his office and

shut the door and sat in his swivel chair. It creaked as he leaned back and allowed himself to close his eyes.

It seemed a long time before he heard a quiet footfall in the vestibule. The office was quite dark as he called out:

"Francisco, is that you? Francisco . . ."

RUTH KRAUSS
Three Poems

My Dream with Its Black Top

My dream with its black top
With its white divider with its curves ahead
My dream with its roll of a ribbon with auras of yellow bird
   with its crosses
My dream between cities
My dream with its wild blue air

Song

(On a Refrain from a Frank O'Hara Song)

Reading about the Wisconsin Weeping Willow
I was thinking of you
and when I saw Plus Free Gifts
I was thinking of you

RUTH KRAUSS, whose poems have appeared in *Harper's* and a number of other periodicals, is best known as an author of children's books, most notably *A Hole Is to Dig* and *I'll Be You (and You Be Me)*. She is married to Crockett Johnson and lives in Connecticut.

and when farther down the page I saw Eat Five Kinds of
    Apples from Just One Miracle Tree
I was thinking of you
I was thinking of you

I'd Much Rather

I'd much rather sit there in the sun
watching the snow drip from the trees
and the milkman's footsteps fill up with water
and the shadow of the spruce tree branches waving
over the sparkle on the leftover snow
and the water dripping in front of my eyes
and the water dripping from the roof
from the bushes of sparkle the water is dripping
the water is dripping from my eyes it is not dripping
I'd much rather sit in the sun the sun
I'd much rather sit in the sun
listening to the shovels scraping
and the birds that whistle on the wires that are dripping
and the backporch is shining
the steam is floating up
the steam floats up around me like my breathing was before
and the maple tree is gleaming in the branches that are bare
above the backporch that is steaming
and I take off my shoes
I take off my stockings and
I sit in the sun I am sitting in the sun
I'd much rather sit here in the sun

GEORGE STEINER
Return No More

He paused by the edge of the road until the truck had curved out of sight and the rasp of the motor had died in the cold salt air.

Then he shifted his rubber-tipped cane to his right hand and stooped down with the left to pick up his suitcase, torn at the hinges and lashed with string.

He advanced in spasms down the graveled side road to the village. His right leg was dead to the hip and swung on the socket of his straining body in a slow arc. The foot, shod in a blunt shoe and raised on a bulky leather heel, slid gratingly with each step. Whereupon the man would again thrust cane and body forward and draw the leg after him.

The twist of effort had hunched his neck and shoulders as if he wore armor, and at every lunge sweat shone at the edge of his fine, reddish hair. Pain and the constant observance of precarious footing fogged his eyes to an uncertain gray. But when he gathered breath, setting his suitcase on the ground and stilting

GEORGE STEINER has published verse, criticism, political essays, and some fiction. He is at present living in England as a Fellow of Churchill College, Cambridge. "Return No More" is one of three novellas, related in theme, which will be published as a single volume by Atheneum.

on his cane like a long-legged heron, his eyes resumed their natural color, a deep harsh blue. The port of his head, with its fine-drawn mouth and delicate bone structure, mocked the gnarled contortion of his gait. The man was handsome in a worn, arresting way.

Ordinarily, trucks did not stop in the highroad but churned by between the dunes and the cliffline, either inland to Rouen, or further along the coast to Le Havre. Yvebecques lay off the road, on the escarpment of the cliffs and along a half-moon of stone beach. High yellow buses stopped on their way from Honfleur, turning into the market place. They unloaded under the wide-flung eaves of the Norman market hall. Beyond its pillared arcade ran a street, narrow and high-gabled, and at the end of it the beach, merging into the wavering light of the sea.

On the market place stood a three-spouted brass fountain. It bore a scroll filled with names and garlanded with ceremonious laurel. Each spout curved like a desolate gargoyle over a date, heavily incised: 1870, 1914, 1939, *pro domo*.

Hearing the truck stop and shift gears, the men who stood among the market stalls or by the fountain looked up. A coldness and stiffness came over their easy stance. The fishmonger, who, was hosing down his marbled stall, let the water race unchecked across his boots.

The traveler was now very near. Once again he rested his suitcase and straightened his back, letting the strain ebb from his shoulders. At the verge of the market place, where the gravel turns to cobblestones, he paused and looked about. His mouth softened into a smile. He had not heard the brusque silence and made for the fountain. He hastened his step by sheer bent of will.

He brought his face under the live spout. The chill, rusty water spilled over his mouth and throat. Then he pushed himself upward, pivoting adroitly on his good leg. He limped toward the red-and-yellow awning of the café. But a mass of long, unmoving shadows fell across his way. Three of the men wore the heavy smocks of fishermen; one was round, close-cropped and in a dark suit. The fifth was scarcely more than a boy. He hovered near the edge of the group and chewed his wet lip.

The stranger looked at them with a grave, hesitant courtesy, as if he had known they would be there to bar his way but had hoped for some twist of grace. The round dark one surged forward. He set his lacquered shoe against the man's cane and thrust his face close. He spoke low, but such was the stillness of the square that his words carried, distinct and raging: "No. No. Not here. Get out. We don't want you back. Any of you, Now get out."

And the boy cried, "No," in a thin, angry whine.

The traveler bent a little to one side, as in a sudden rouse of wind. Close by a voice flat with rage said again: "Get out. We don't want any part of you. Lucky for you you're a cripple. Not enough meat for a man on your carcass."

He squinted against the high sun and remembered his bearings. He veered from the bristling shadows and started toward the street which led from the market square to the apple orchards on the western terrace of the cliffs. But even before he had entered the dark of the Rue de la Poissonière, the boy had leaped past. He whirled, grinning with spite: "I know where you are going. I will tell them. They'll stone you alive." He spurted on and turned once more: "Why don't you catch me, cripple?"

Tight-buttoned, the notary peered after the stranger. Then he spat between his lacquered toes and whistled. A large dog rose from under the meat stalls and ambled over. A leathery cur backed mournfully from a pile of fishgut oozing on the warm stones. Other dogs came off their haunches. The notary scratched his mongrel behind the ears and hissed at it, pointing toward the limping man. Then he flicked the dog across its snout with a lash of the wrist. The animal sprang away snarling. Monsieur Lurôt hissed again and the dog understood. He fanged the fleas from his raw neck and gave a queer yelp, cruel and lost. A retriever, who had been drowsing under the billiard table, tore out of the café. Now other men were flailing and whistling at the dogs and pointing to the Rue de la Poissonière. The pack milled at the fountain snapping at each other, then hurtled toward the narrow street. In the van, Lurôt's mongrel let out a full-throated cry.

He heard them coming in a loud rush but they were at his

heels before he could turn. They flew at him like crazed shadows, slobbering and snapping the air with woken fury. The man swayed off balance as he swung his cane at the bellowing pack. He was able to stem his legs against a wall but the mongrel sprang at him, its eyes flaring with vacant malignity. The rancid scent of the dog enveloped him. He flung the animal from his face but felt a hot scratch raking his shoulder.

Beyond the reek and clamor of the charging dogs, like distant streamers on the wind, the lame man heard laughter from the market place.

The animals were wearying of their sport. They stood off, baring their teeth. Only the retriever was still at him, circling and darting in, its head low. It evaded the man's cane with jagged leaps. Suddenly the bitch hurled herself at the stranger's inert leg. Her teeth locked on the leather heel. The man went down against the side of the house, clawing the air for support. The dog inched back, its tongue red over its bruised mouth. The cane snapped down on it with a single, murderous stroke. The animal subsided into a moaning heap; somewhere a bone had cracked and now its eyes spun.

The suitcase had fallen on the cobblestones. One of the hinges sprung and a small parcel tumbled out. It had shattered against the sharp rim of the pavement. Slivers of blue and ice-white china lay dispersed in the gutter. In the murky street they gathered points of light. The man dragged himself over and picked up what was left of the Meissen figurine. Only the base, with its frieze of pale cornflowers, and the slim, silk-hosed legs of the shepherd dancer were intact. Bereft of the arching body and dreaming visage, these legs, in their plum breeches and black pumps, retained the motion of the dance. The head had smashed into myriad pieces; only the hat could be made out, lying near the middle of the street, three-cornered and with a flash of plume.

The traveler lurched to his feet, picked up his suitcase and tightened the string over the broken corner. The dogs stood wary. Then the mongrel shuffled near and whined softly. The man passed his hand over its mangy ears. Lurôt's dog looked up with a wide, stupid stare. The pack did not follow the cripple as he moved away.

Before him the houses thinned out and the cliff towered into full view. The sea lay to the right, murmurous and hazy under the white sun. The salt wind dried the sweat from the man's face and body. But the yelp of the dogs had bitten into his marrow, and dim shocks of fear and tiredness passed through his limbs. In the sudden shade of the apple trees his skin prickled with cold. Now the path lifted again and the sea opened beneath him, glittering in the heat. Only the tideline moved, lapping the beach with a sullen vague rustle.

The way dipped into a hollow. Bees sang between the stubble and the grass had the dry savor of inland. Recollection came upon him vivid and exact. *Quis viridi fontes induceret umbra*— who shall veil the spring with shadow and leaf?

It was at this spot that the Latin tag had risen out of a school-boy's harried forgetting. And its music had held through the mad clamor. He had hobbled his dawn round of the fortifications on the rim of the cliffs, inspecting the bunkers sunk into live rock, and peering through the range finder at the still haze on the Channel. He was returning to his quarters at the farm of La Hurlette. The path was staked between mine fields, and high in the booming air he could hear planes moving down the valley of the Seine on their daily, mounting runs. Far away, on the river bluffs above Rouen, antiaircraft guns were firing short bursts. The detonations thudded as from a distant quarry.

As he had limped into the dell, all sounds had receded. He had sat down to still the rack of his body. His wound was new, and he had suffered hideously in the field hospital near Khar-khov and on the trains that wormed across Europe, furtively, with jolting detours over railbeds and bridges twisted by bombs. He had lain on a siding at the approaches to Breslau watching a bottle of morphine teeter on the shelf out of reach of his fin-gers. The orderlies were cowering in a ditch.

He had learned to live with his pain as one lives with a famil-iar yet treacherous animal. He conceived of it as a large cat which honed its claws, drawing them like slow fire from shoulder to heel, and then crouching down again in the dim and middle of his body. He had been posted to the Yvebecques sector of the Channel wall as chief of military intelligence. It was a soft billet accorded in deference to his infirmity. As the pain slunk back to its lair, that line of Virgil had sung in his bruised thoughts. With it the gate of memory swung open and behind it drowsed the rust-green gables and slow canals of the north country.

Later that year the Channel haze had reddened into savage tumult. But through the hell that ensued, he carried the verse with him, and the image of this place, a hand cupped full of silence and water, guarded from the wind.

As he came out of the hollow, still grasping his suitcase, Falk's eyes lit. La Hurlette lay just beyond the next fold in the down, where the cliff subsided under green ridges and the valley of the Coutances opened out. He could see the stream, quick and chalk-pale between marsh grass. Now the farm was in sight and recognition beat at him like a wing stroke.

The pockmarks made by mortar shells were still visible under the eaves, but rounded by time, as if clams had dug their delicate houses in the stone. The byre shone with a new red roof but the outbuildings and the clumps of lilac and holly were exactly as he had last seen them, hurtling by in a motorcycle side-car, under wild, acid smoke, five summers ago.

Then he saw the ash tree to the left of the house and his spirit went molten. It stood in leaf, more gray now than silver. Through the foliage he could make out, unmistakable, the stab of the branch on which they had hanged Jean Terrenoire. The night the invasion had begun on the beaches to the west, a patrol had caught the boy perched near the summit of the cliff. He was signaling to the shadows at sea. They had carried him back to La Hurlette, his face beaten livid with their rifle butts. Falk sought to question him but he merely spat out his teeth. So they let the family out of the cellar for a moment to say good-bye and then dragged him to the ash tree. Falk had seen the thing done.

The tree had thickened but the branch retained its dragon motion and Falk could not take his eyes from it. As he started toward the house, he remembered suddenly that the Terrenoires would be waiting. The boy from the market place had scurried before him to give warning. They would be at his throat before he could cross the threshold. Hatred lay across his path like an unsteady glare. Forcing back his shoulders, Falk glanced at the window of the corner room, his room, and saw the foxglove on the sill, as he had left it. Here had been his island in the ravening sea, here she had brought him the warm, grass-scented milk in a blue pitcher. He pressed on.

The door was loose on the latch and Falk stopped, nakedly afraid. He was momentarily blinded by the dark of the house but knew almost at once that nothing had been altered. The pots and warming pans glowed on the wall like cuirasses of a ghostly troop. An odor of wax cloth and mouldering cheese hung over the room, and its subtle bite had stayed in his nostrils. The clock which he had bought during his convalescence in Dresden and which the Terrenoires had accepted when first he came, with neither thanks nor refusal, hammered softly on the mantelpiece.

Then he saw Blaise. He stood by the wall and in his fist Falk glimpsed the black fire iron. Blaise stared at him, his tight mouth wrenched with hatred and disbelief: "Mother of God! The half-wit wasn't lying. It *is* you. You've dared come back. You've dared crawl out here. You stinking, murdering pile of shit!" He swayed nearer: "So you've come back. *Ordure! Salaud!*" The mind's ex-crement of hate poured out of Blaise. He gasped for air as if rage held him by the windpipe. "I'm going to kill you. You know that, don't you? I'm going to kill you."

He reared back, his eyes crazy and hot, and lifted the iron. But old Terrenoire flung a chair at him, across the floor of the kitchen: "Stop it! *Merde.* Who do you think runs this house?" He had gone gray and sere; age had sanded down his beak nose. But the old, cunning mastery was still there, and Blaise winced as if the whip had caught him on the mouth. "No one's going to do any killing around here unless I tell them to. Remember what I said. Don't drive the fox away if you want his pelt. Per-haps Monsieur Falk has something to say to us." He looked at his guest with heavy, watchful scorn.

A low wail broke from Blaise's clenched throat: "I don't care what he says. I'll flay the hide off the stinking swine." He crouched near the fireplace like a numbed adder, venomous but unmoving.

As Falk limped toward the bench in the opaque terror of a slow, familiar dream, he saw the woman and the two girls. Madame Terrenoire's ears stood out from beneath gray, wiry hair. There were tufts of white above her eyes. Nicole had kept her straight carriage but a spinsterish tautness lay about her thin neck. Falk saw that her hands were trembling.

Danielle had turned her back. Falk bore her image with him, inviolate and precise. But it was that of a twelve-year-old. She had large gray eyes and her hair shed the heavy light of hammered gold. She had not been beautiful, having her father's nose and angular shoulders. But she possessed a darting grace of life. They spoke together often, in a hushed, courtly manner. She brought him breakfast and stole to the corner of the room to watch his orderly wax his boots and mounted heel. She did not sit by him, but stood grave and malicious, as little girls do in front of old, broken men. Every morning Falk took coffee beans and a spoonful of sugar from his rations and set them at the rim of his tray. He knew she would carry these spoils of love to her father, racing noiselessly down the stairs.

On the day of the invasion, against the whine and roar of coastal batteries, Danielle had slipped into his room. Falk was putting on his helmet and greatcoat before going to the command car camouflaged under the oak trees a thousand yards from the house. She watched him warily, the floodboards shaking to the sound of the guns. As he turned to go, easing the strap of the automatic pistol over his shoulder, she touched his sleeve with a furtive, sensuous motion. Before he could say anything she was gone, and he heard the cellar door slam heavily behind her quick steps.

He had seen her once more that night. Through his torn lips Jean Terrenoire said nothing to his family. He merely embraced each in turn while the corporal knotted the rope. Coming to Danielle, Jean knelt down and stroked her cheek. She shivered wildly in his grasp. They hurried him into the garden. As Falk passed, the girl shrank from him and made a low, inhuman sound. It had stuck in his mind like a festering thorn. Now he hardly dared look at her. But he knew at a glance that she had grown tall and that her hair still burned like autumn.

Falk sagged to the low bench. He laid the cane on the floor, under the crook of his dead leg.

"You are right. There is something I want to say to you." He looked at Blaise, coiled near him, murderous. "I pray God you will give me the time."

A black stillness was in the room. "When I left you, I had orders to reach Cuverville and re-establish Brigade headquarters. But at daylight American fighters strafed us. They came in so close to the ground that haystacks scattered under their wings. On the second pass they got Bültner, my orderly. You remember Bültner. He was a fat man and ate the green aples where they fell in the orchard. I think he was secretly in love with you, Nicole. Anyway, he was so badly hit that we dared not move him, but left him under the hedgerow propped on a blanket. I hoped the ambulance would find him in time. But some of your people got to him first. Later on we heard that they beat him to death with threshing flails.

"We could not stay in Cuverville and were dispatched to Rouen. I remember the two spires in the red smoke. An hour after we arrived, paratroopers came down in the middle of the city. Each day was the same: we moved east and there were fewer of us. In good weather the planes were at us incessantly, like a pack of wolves. We had respite only when the clouds came low. I grew to hate the sun as if it had the face of death.

"Each man has his own private surrender. At some point he knows inside himself that he is beaten. I knew when I saw what was left of Aachen. But we kept the knowledge from each other as if it was a secret malady. And we fought on. During our counterattack in the winter I was in sight of Strasbourg. The next day my wound ripped open again. I was no further use to anyone and they shipped me back to a convalescent home, somewhere near Bonn, in a patch of wood. The windows had been blown to bits and we tacked army blankets across the frames to keep out the snow. We sat in that false dark hearing the big guns get closer. Then we heard tank treads on the road. That day the medical staff and the nurses vanished. The old doctor stayed. He said he was tired of running: had run all the way to Moscow and back. He had a bottle of brandy in front of him and would wait. He gave me my discharge papers. Some of our infantry set up a mortar in the courtyard of the house and the Americans had to use flame-throwers to get them out. I do not know what happened to the old man."

Falk shifted his weight. The sun was moving west and the light slid across the window like a long red fox.

"I had to get to Hamburg. I wanted to see my home. There had been rumors about the fire raids and I was anxious. I hardly remember how I managed to get on to a train, one of the last traveling north from Berlin. I had grown up in Hamburg and knew it like the lineaments of my own hand. What I saw when I crawled across the rubble of the station yard was unimaginable, but also terribly familiar. When I was a small boy, the teacher had tacked a greatly enlarged photograph of the moon on our classroom wall. I used to stare at it interminably, and the craters, striations and seas of dead ash were fixed in my brain. Now they lay before me. The whole city was on fire. There was no sunlight, no sky, only swirls of gray air, so hot it burned one's lips. The houses had settled into vast craters. They burned day and night homing the planes to their target. But there were no more targets; only a sea of flame spreading windward with each successive raid. And wherever the ruins grew hottest, gusts of air rushed in, poisonous with stench and ash.

"I must have started yelling or running about, for a shadow came at me out of the smoke and shook me hard. It was a one-armed man in a dented helmet. He told me to get down to a shelter before the next wave passed over. The sirens were wailing again but I could barely hear them above the noise of the flames. I did not know until then that fire makes that sound—a queer hideous scratching, as if blood were seething in one's throat. The man pulled me by the sleeve: he was a warden in the police auxiliary: I was to obey him; he couldn't waste his time looking after damn fools who didn't take shelter.

"We scuttled down into a trench lined with sandbags and sheets of corrugated iron. It was full of smoke and rancid smells. I made out gray splotches in the dark. They were human faces. At first I thought they were wearing gas masks or goggles. But it was simply that they were black with soot and that the near flames had left livid streaks on their skin. Only their eyes were alive; they closed suddenly when the bombs fell. There was a small girl crouching near the open end of the trench. She was barefoot and had burn marks on her arms. She asked me for a cigarette, saying she was hungry. I had none but gave her a wafer of Dutch chocolate wrapped in silver foil. She broke it in two, thrusting one piece in her pocket and placing the other in her mouth. She sucked at it cautiously. It was still on her tongue when the all-clear sounded. She heard it before any of us, raced up the steps and disappeared into the stinging smoke. As I clambered from the trench, I saw her running beside a burning wall. She turned back and waved.

"I asked the warden how I might get to the Geiringerstrasse. He gave me a frightened, angry look. 'Isn't that where the gas tanks are?' I remembered the two grimy tanks and the wire fence around them at the upper end of the street where the foundry works began. 'The tanks are near there, yes.' 'That's what I thought. No use your going. It's all sealed off. The *Amis* have been after those gas tanks with incendiaries. They got them two days ago. No one has been allowed near the Geiringerstrasse since. Come along. We'll have a look at your papers and find you a shelter to sleep in.' But I shook him loose and hastened for home.

"New fires had driven the smoke upward and guided me like wildly swinging lamps. In the burning craters single houses or parts of houses still stood upright. The passage of flame had traced strange designs on the walls, as if a black ivy had sprung up. Often I had to step across the dead. Some had been burned alive trapped by curtains of fire; others had been blown to pieces or struck by shrapnel. But many lay outwardly unhurt, their mouths wide open. They had died of suffocation when the flames drank the air. I saw a young boy who must have died actually breathing fire; it had singed his mouth and leaped down his throat, blackening the flesh. Scorched into the asphalt next to him was the brown shadow of a cat.

"As I drew near what had been the Löwenplatz and the beginning of the Geiringerstrasse, a cordon of men barred my way. They were Gestapo and police. They had guns and were letting no one pass. Behind them the fires burned white with a fantastic glitter. Even here, at the end of the street, the heat and stench of gas were unbearable. The heat flogged one across the eyes and nose with nauseating strokes. I felt vomit in my mouth and grew hysterical. I pleaded with one of the Gestapo officers. I must get through. My family might be trapped in there. He shook his head and whispered at me; he was too tired to speak; he had had no sleep since three nights; since the gas tanks went up. No one was allowed through. His men were in there now seeing what could be done. At that moment I heard shots being fired somewhere in the street, behind the wall of flame. I began yelling and trying to wrestle my way through the cordon. One of the policemen took me by the collar: 'Don't be an idiot. There's nothing more we can do. We've tried everything. We're putting them out of their misery. They're begging for a bullet.' And now the burning wind brought voices, high-pitched, mad voices. The line of policemen flinched. Two Gestapo men shuffled out of the smoke and tore off their masks. They carried guns. One of them went over to a pile of rubble and fainted. The other stood in front of the officer swaying like a drunk: 'I can't go on with it, Herr Gruppen-führer, I can't' He shambled away in a sleepwalker's gait, dropping his gun. The officer turned to me with an odd look. 'You say you have some of people in there? All right. Take that pistol and come with me. Perhaps you *can* help.' His eyes were like two red embers; there was no life in them, only smoke and fear. We put on masks and hunched through the searing wind. The Geir-ingerstrasse runs alongside a small canal. It was always full of oil and slag. As a boy I used to watch the sunlight break on the oil in blues and bright greens. Now, crawling forward under the blaze of the gas tanks, I saw the canal again. There were human beings in it, standing immersed up to their necks. They saw us coming and began waving their arms. But instantly they plunged their arms back into the water, screaming. The Gestapo officer lifted a corner of his mask and rasped at me: 'Phosphorus.' The Americans had dropped incendiaries made of phosphorus. Where it is in contact with air phosphorus burns unquenchably. Their clothes and bodies on fire, the people of the Geiringerstrasse had died like living torches. But a few had managed to leap into the canal. There they stood for three days. Every time they tried to crawl out of the water their clothing flared up in a yellow flame.

In the heart of the fire they were dying of cold and hunger. While the freezing water slid over them, their bodies shook with burns and mad spasms. Most had given up and gone under. But a few were still erect, yelling hoarsely for food and help. The Red Cross had fed them from the banks and put blankets around their heads. But on the third day, as the raids started again, everyone had been ordered out. Nothing could be done except to make death quicker and stop the inhuman screaming. So the Gestapo went in. Most of the faces were unrecognizable. Hair and eyebrows had been seared away. On the black water I saw a row of living skulls. The Gestapo officer had drawn his pistol and I heard him firing. One of the faces was staring at me. It was a girl, and on her scorched forehead the flames had left a tuft of hair, red like mine. Her lips were baked and swollen but she was trying to form words. I crept over to her and took off my mask. The heat and reek of phosphorus made me gag. But I was able to lean out over the canal and she drifted toward me, her eyes never leaving mine. Her tongue was a charred stump but I understood what she was saying. 'Quickly. Please. Quickly.' I slipped my arm behind her head and put my lips to hers. She leaned back and closed her eyes. Then I shot her. I can't be sure. The faces were too far gone. Yet I am sure it was my sister."

The room was still as winter. In the gathered shadows the chime of the clock had grown remote and unreal. Suddenly Danielle spoke, without turning around, loud into the dark air: "Good. Good. I am glad."

Her voice sprang at Falk out of an ambush long dreaded but now intolerable. The hatred of it stunned him. It seemed to close over his head in a suffocating tide. The pain that had been lurking in his bent, immobile leg surged to a shrill pitch. It shot into his back and set his neck in a vise. The drag and harshness of the long day racked his will. Only the pain was real, like a red fist before his eyes, and it beat toward the ground. But even at the instant where something inside him, something of the quick of hope and bearing, was about to break, Danielle rose and moved swiftly past him. Her hand brushed against his sleeve in dim remembrance.

Falk raised his head to look after her and the pain grew bearable, ebbing into his hips, where it gnawed in sharp but familiar guise. Terrenoire got up and lit the lamp on the sideboard. It threw the shadow of his hooked nose against the wall like a child's drawing of a pirate. Madame Terrenoire and Nicole cleared the dishes, stacking the white and blue china. They did not look at the crippled man on the bench.

Blaise came off his haunches, his cat's eyes livid. He spat at Falk's clubfoot with derisive loathing and swore under his breath: *"Nom de Dieu."* Then he picked up the milk pail in an easy motion and went out the door. Before it swung close, Falk caught a glimpse of the early stars.

*

He woke with a numb jolt. The sourness of broken sleep lay thick on his tongue. Momentarily he did not know where he was. Night was in the room and the events of the past few hours passed vaguely through his thoughts. Then he saw a shadow looming at him out of the stairwell. On guard, Falk groped for his cane. His fingers tightened on the grip, but nearly at once he recognized a familiar patch of white lace; Madame Terrenoire's nightcap, and beneath it the flat, coarse features of the aging woman. She rustled toward him in her frayed houserobe, leaned against the stove and searched him out with her shallow eyes. Her scrutiny slid over him like a blind man's hand, neutral yet inquisitive.

Then she asked abruptly "Why have you come back here? Was it to tell us that vile story . . . *cette sale histoire?"*

"Yes," said Falk.

"Is the story true?"

"Yes," he said again, beyond outrage.

"You are lying," she said, not in anger, but with malignity. "You are lying. You didn't come back here just to tell us what happened to you. Why should we care? You've come back to take something from us. I know your kind. That's all you're good for. To take and take and take." The hands in her lap opened and closed rapaciously.

"You have so much to give," said Falk.

She arched like an old cat: "Not any more. You've taken it all. You took Jean and hanged him on that cursed tree. You took so many of our young men that Nicole has been left a spinster. Just look at her. She'll soon be dry wood. Blaise is a ruffian. He was never meant to be an oldest son. When you killed Jean there was no one else for us to lean on. It's made him a brute. And what about me? I'm an old woman. There's hardly anyone left around here except the children and the old. You took the rest and hanged them on the trees. No, there's nothing more to take." She closed her mouth hard, and to Falk she seemed like an astute fish snapping for air and then diving back into silence.

"Perhaps it's my turn to give. Giving and taking . . . *c'est parfois la même chose*. It's sometimes the same act." She brushed the thought aside with a contemptuous flutter of her hand.

But Falk persisted: "It was easy to take. Too easy. We must learn to receive from each other." She gave no sign of comprehension. "It may be that you are right, that I have come to take again. But what I can take from you this time is not life. It is some part of the death that lies between us. *Un peu de cette mort.*"

She countered relentlessly: "I don't understand you. Taking is taking."

"Even when it is love?" Falk asked awkwardly.

She gave a dry laugh: *"Vous êtes de beaux salauds.* You're a fine lot of swine. To speak of love in a house where you've murdered a child."

"But that is exactly the house in which I must speak of it. Don't you see? After everything that's happened, where else can it have any meaning?"

Something in his vehemence stung her but she yielded no ground: "You talk like a priest, but I know you for what you are. How could I forget? You killed Jean. Out there, on that ash tree."

"None of us are what we were. Try me again."

She shrugged him off: "What for? Leave us alone. There's no place for your kind among us. We've seen you too often. You've been at our throats three times. *Ça suffit.*"

She turned from him with distaste as if she had expended too richly from her small hoard of words. But at the foot of the stairs she paused and after a spell turned with a queer jerk: "That bench can't be much good for sleeping. You look as stiff as a dead mackerel. God knows why I'm letting you spend the night here." Yet even as she said it, a note of pleased cunning stole into her hacking voice: "There's a room at the top of the house, with a bed in it. I don't have to show *you* the way." Madame Terrenoire started up the wooden stairs. Falk hobbled across the kitchen. She waited for him to come near, looked back and said between her teeth: "It was Jean's bed. See whether you can sleep in it, Captain."

Having reached the musty room under the gables, Falk looked out the window and saw the moon in the orchard. Beyond the brittle noise of the crickets he caught the grating of the sea. He sat there for a long time, scarcely breathing the stale, warm air. When at last he fell back on the bedspread, the first glint of sunrise was visible on the eastern cliffs like a thread of copper in the morning grass.

*

The moment of pure, unthinking vengeance had passed. Werner Falk was endured at La Hurlette like one of those masterless dogs who forage at the edge of a farm. Hatred crackled under his feet in vicious spurts. Blaise was dark with outrage and the old woman looked on Falk with a patient contempt more insidious than fury. But they did not touch him when he passed in reach of the scythe or the heavy spade. The hideousness of his tale, the offering of it in exchange of grief, gave him sanctuary. Though they were only obscurely aware of it, the Terrenoires treated Falk as if there was on his skin the white shadow of leprosy.

Terrenoire himself said nothing. He observed Falk with gloomy complaisance; he discerned in his queer, unbidden arrival a hint of vantage. Nicole cast words at Falk now and again, and when they stood near each other a low flame lit in her sallow cheeks. She gazed after him when he trailed off to the steaming fields in the hot of the morning and threw him a nervous, irritated look when he returned at twilight from the cliffs. Only Danielle stayed outside the wary game. When they chanced to meet in the stairwell or across the neutral ground of the kitchen, her eyes narrowed with pain.

In the village voices rose and fell. Everyone knew that the German captain had returned to La Hurlette and that his presence there was being suffered in the very shade of the ash tree. Around Lurôt's table at the Café du Vieux Port anger and wonderment eddied. But the Terrenoires were regarded as deep ones. Drawing the pale white wine through his lips, Lurôt concluded that there was doubtless something to be reaped from Falk's visit. The Terrenoires were no fools; *ce ne sont pas des poires.* Vague, covetous suspicion hardened to belief: Falk had come to pay compensation for Jean's death. The Germans were rich now, filthy rich. What had he carried in his suitcase? Some of the banknotes and jewelry which the boches had looted from France. There would be a new plow soon at La Hurlette.

So the villagers waited and pondered, like a herd of cattle, pawing the earth now and again in drowsy malevolence. They bore Falk's coming and going, though a sullen tremor ran under their skin as he passed. Soon they paid no heed and were hardly aware of the limping figure that emerged from the orchards to sit on the stone beach in the glitter of noon.

After three o'clock the tide receded nearly to the base of the cliff gate, leaving behind a green, shimmering expanse. Women and children swarmed out to harvest shrimp and mussels. Falk delighted in their scurrying progress and the swift fall of the nets. Often he hobbled a short distance into the unsteady ooze of stone and trapped sea.

A week after his arrival at La Hurlette he saw Nicole just ahead of him, her skirts tucked high. She turned and called under her breath: *"Venez donc.* Come on out."

He followed precariously. Weed-covered and smoothed by the tides, the rocks were like glass. Between them lay brackish puddles. The afternoon sun played brokenly on the water, and rock and sand flickered like a mosaic. Falk slithered to his knees in the tangle of red weeds. Nicole stayed just in front of him, flinging words over her shoulder so that he had to strain after them.

"The others are wondering why you've come back. Blaise wanted to kill you on the spot. He still does. But I won't let him." She turned for an instant, her face strangely flushed. "I told *maman* you had no other place to go. All your people in Hamburg are dead. We're the closest thing you have to a home." He caught the abrupt laugh in her voice: "It sounds mad, doesn't it? But I'm sure it's true. You were happy at La Hurlette. We knew that. I think that's why Jean hated you so much. If only you had been unhappy among us or treated us badly, we could have borne it. But to see you come through the door in your gray coat as if it was really home to you, as if you were at peace, that was unendurable. You were terribly good-looking then. Do you know that? It made it worse."

Falk slid grotesquely into a trough of bubbling sand but her arm swung back and held him. They stood beside each other on a rock at the edge of the flats. Before them the sea heaved in a drowsy swell. All around the herring gulls yawped and scoured for their prey. Nicole lifted her chin into the wind: "We were all afraid of you. We had to be. But Jean hated you. Perhaps because he admired you so much; for being an officer and for the books you brought with you. He used to steal up to your room and read them while you were away. I wonder whether you knew." Falk did not answer but bent close to catch her words amid the hiss of the returning sea. "He tried to read the books of German poetry. And the thick one in the yellow wrapper. It was by a philosopher, wasn't it? With a long name. I don't remember. It drove Jean crazy to think you could have such books and treasure them. He wanted to kill you. It wouldn't have been so difficult either. The way you used to come down alone from the cliff at nightfall. But they wouldn't let him."

"They?"

"The cell he belonged to, the *réseau* he took orders from in Le Havre. They didn't believe in acts of individual terrorism. Or so they claimed."

"Who were they?"

"Surely you knew. Jean was in the Party."

She faced him, her mouth drawn thin. "He was a rabid communist. We thought you had found out. That's why you hanged him, wasn't it?"

Falk shook his head and tried to keep his footing on the wet rock: "No, we had no knowledge of that. We hanged your brother because he was signaling to the Canadian landing barges from the top of the cliff."

"Ah. Was that the only reason? *Qu-importe?* He wanted to kill you and you killed him instead. That's war, isn't it?" She said it with indifference, as if it was a truth long buried. "Father had no love for Jean. They fought like dogs. When he discovered that Jean was going around with communists, he beat him half to death. But Jean grew to be stronger than *papa*. He didn't dare lay a hand on him later on. So they snarled at each other continually."

"What about you, Nicole? Did you get on with Jean?"

"No," she said. "I'm not a hypocrite like the others. So I'll tell you. We never cared much for each other. I was the oldest but he showed me no regard. With his books and glib talk and stupid politics, you would have thought he was some kind of genius. But he wasn't. I'd say he was an arrogant puppy and that's the truth. No, there was no love lost between us. He knew I was plain-looking and used to joke about it with the other louts in the village. Said I was tall and bony as an old rake; that's what they whispered behind my back, *vieux râteau*. After you came I suddenly realized that Jean was nothing but a little boy, a clever little boy playing at war. I told him how good-looking you were and that you were a real soldier. It made him livid." Nicole glanced away in vexed remembrance. "When you killed him, I knew that I should feel bitter grief. But I felt nothing. Nothing at all. Danielle howled for days. We couldn't get her to eat or take her dirty clothes off. She adored Jean. She was the only one of us to whom he was gentle and they had all sorts of secrets. But I felt nothing. When the invasion came that morning, I had only one thought: perhaps I shall survive, perhaps there is going to be an end to this terrible time."

"So that's why you've forgiven me," said Falk.

"Forgiven? *Il n'est pas question de ça.* I'm no priest. I'm not interested in the past. I wish the past had never been. We must start living again. What have we to do with the dead? That's why you've come back, isn't it? You've come back to La Hurlette to show that the past need not matter, that we can salvage from it what was good and leave the rest behind like a bad dream, haven't you?" She flung the question at him with a sudden imperious surge, as if opening to the wind a hidden banner. Falk was startled by the intensity of life in her sharp features.

She bore in on him: "That's what I've told them at home. Let him be. He's going to stay with us and make good for the past. Blaise and *papa* think you're going to pay them or make some kind of cosy deal. The fools. They must think you sell cider in Germany!" Her gaiety stung. "But let them think that. It will give us time." Her hand touched his in fierce, shy demand. Falk saw the waters rising and said nothing.

Nicole lashed out at his silence: "Why don't you say something?" Her lips whitened and she drew nearer to him. "Why don't you look me in the face?"

Her nakedness appalled him. He spoke her name softly and in fear, as if it was an open wound: "Nicole. You've understood many things which I've felt. You've said the things for which I found no right words. But I don't think there can be between us . . ." He stared at the moving sand, "I don't think you and I, however close we must be to one another . . ."

Their faces were only inches apart. "You don't think that you and I . . ." Nicole stared at him bewildered. "Not you and I . . . Why then have you come back?" Falk reached toward her but she flinched away. "What are you doing here? What kind of a foul trick are you playing on us?"

"I know," said Falk, "it doesn't make sense. I am like a sleepwalker looking for that which kept me alive in the daytime. Looking for the one door that opens out of night. Probably I shan't be allowed anywhere near it. It's madness, I know. But you will understand, Nicole. You must understand."

She had already begun moving away. Her face had gone ashen. Only her eyes were alive and brimming with pain. Falk had once seen a gunner whip a horse across the eyes and he remembered the glare of anguish.

"Listen to me, Nicole, I beg you. I need your help. I need to know that you do not hate me. Without you I shall be hounded away from here. Just listen to me for a moment. Please."

He called in vain. The girl was racing back toward the beach, skipping with grim agility from rock to rock. She glanced back at him only once, but across the gap of wind and spray he could see the fury in her. When he looked up again, he realized he was alone. The other fishermen were hastening landward. Over the entire flats and in the dark pools the water was seething in annunciation of the returning tide. The gulls were veering towards their nests in the high cliff and the sun glowed red on their wings. Falk saw that the sea was close upon him. He clambered toward the shore. But the tide was quicker. It sent sheets of foam flashing past him and the rocks grew vague under the charge and retreat of the surf. Crabs rose warily out of the quaking mud and scuttled away from his groping steps. He fell and slithered and drew himself up again, but the water sucked at his weight. Despite the chill wind, he was drenched with sweat. Soon his hands, grasping their way along the rock edges, were raw and torn. The salt bit into his broken nails. In the failing light the beach grew distant and the roofs took on a remote, mocking blue. Laboring against the undertow, Falk remembered an ugly moment south of Smolensk. In pursuit of the Russians, his company had tumbled into marsh. Unable to keep rank in the knife-edged grass, sickened by the flies and the stench of dead water, he and his men had crawled forward on their bellies, looking for steady ground. The enemy had turned on them with mortar fire. Wherever the shells dropped, stinking water sprayed over the wounded and the dead. Clawing his way through the lashing surf, his hands bloodied, Falk remembered the episode. The knowledge that he had got out alive screwed his will to a last, fierce effort. He lunged out of the flailing tide and on to the pebbles. On hands and knees he drew himself to a pile of nets drying in the late sun and looked back. The sea was yelping at the shore like a pack of foxes: its cold tongue darted at him still.

Nicole had raced blindly through the orchards. She met Danielle on the stairs and said in a strangled voice: "It's you he's after. It's you. Make the best of it, *petite garce*." Danielle stared at her in bewildered protest and raised her hand as if to ward off a blow. But all she felt were Nicole's fingers brushing her forehead in ironic benediction.

*

The next morning Terrenoire broke his silence. Falk had watched him feeding a sow as she hammered her pink snout against the trough. Closing the wire fence behind him, Terrenoire asked, "How long are you planning to stay with us, Monsieur Falk?" And before Falk could reply: "Not that it bothers me. It's no skin off my back. I told Clotilde you would be paying for your room and board, and paying better than last time. But you seem to be stirring up the girls, just like you did when you first came. They're running about like crazy hens. *Et parbleu*, you must admit it's a strange place for you to choose for a holiday."

"I'm not here for a holiday," said Falk; "it's more serious than that. In fact, it's the only completely serious thing I've ever tried to do."

Terrenoire blinked peevishly at the implication of obscure, private motive.

"I grew up in a kind of very loud bad dream," said Falk. "I cannot remember a time when we were not marching or shouting and when there were no flags in the street. When I think of my childhood all I can remember distinctly are the drums and the uniform I wore as a young pioneer. And the great red flags with the white circle and the black hooked cross in the middle. They were constantly draped across our window. It seems to me I always saw the sun through a red curtain. And I remember the torches. One night my father woke me suddenly and tore me to the window. The whole street was full of men marching with torches like a great fiery worm. I must have yelled with fear or sleepiness and my father slapped me across the mouth. I don't remember much about him but he smelled of leather.

"School was worse. The drums beat louder and there were more flags. On the way home we played rabbit hunt and went after Jews. We made them run in the gutter carrying our books and if they dropped any we held them down and pissed in their

faces. In the summer we were taught how to be men. They sat
us on a log two by two. Every boy in turn would slap his partner as hard as he could. First one to duck was a coward. I passed
out once but did not fall off the log. I never finished school. I
suppose my final exam came in Lemberg when they told me to
clean out a bunker with a flame-thrower. I had my graduation
in Warsaw, marching with the victory parade. Now the drums
never stopped. They were always pounding at us: in Norway;
outside Utrecht, where I got my first wound; in Salonika, where
we hanged the partisans on meat hooks; and at Kharkov, where
this happened." Falk's hand trailed absently along his leg.

"They never stopped, and in the hospital outside Dresden I
thought they would drive me mad. I can't tell you much about
it, Monsieur Terrenoire, because I hardly remember it myself.
There were two of me. One night I came hobbling down the ward
back from the latrine. There was no bed vacant. I must have
hopped from bed to bed looking. Then I remembered that my
fever chart had a number. I found it. There was another man in
my bed. I saw the stain seeping along his bandaged leg and knew
that this man was I. So I jumped on him and tried to get at his
throat. After that they kept me under morphine."

They had strayed into the orchard. Falk went on: "Then I
was sent here. How can I explain? In church they tell us that
Lazarus rose from his stinking shroud having been four days
dead. And they call *that* a miracle! I had been dead twenty years.
I did not really know that there was such a thing as life. No one
had told me. I first stumbled on that dangerous secret here, at
La Hurlette. You probably don't even remember the first night
I spent with you."

Terrenoire looked at him guardedly: "I can't say I do."

Falk laughed, his voice exultant: "Why should you? It was a
night like many others. Officers had been billeted here before I
came. To you it meant nothing: just another unwelcome stranger in the house. But for me it was the first hour of grace. I stood
up there at the window under the gables, looked across the orchard and caught a flash of the sea. Danielle—do you remember
how slight and small she was?—rapped at my door and brought
me a pitcher of milk. It was a blue pitcher and the milk was

warm. I know these are all perfectly ordinary things, a room with a low ceiling, a row of apple trees and a blue pitcher. But to me, at that moment, they were the gates of life. *Lazare, veni foras.* But that man had been dead only four days! In this house I rose from a death much longer and worse. That night, when Danielle set the pitcher down on the table, the drums stopped beating for the first time. I never heard them here. Oh, I know the war was everywhere around us, that there were mines at the end of the garden, and barbed wire on the cliffs. But it didn't seem to matter. I saw life sitting in your kitchen as if it was a brightness. Isn't that an absurd thought? But those who have grown up dead have such visions. And because the drums had stopped, I began hearing myself. I had never really heard my own voice before. Only other men's shouts and the echo we had to give. That's all I had been taught to do, echo shout for shout and hatred for hatred. It sounds fantastic, I know, but watching you and your children, I realized that human beings don't always shout at each other. The silence in this house was like fresh water, I plunged my hands and face in it. And I discovered that men are not always either one's friends or one's enemies, but somewhere in between. They had forgotten to tell us that in the *Hitlerjugend* and the *Wehrmacht.*" Falk thrust his hand among the powdery blossoms. "This is where I climbed out of the grave, Monsieur Terrenoire, in your house and among these trees."

Terrenoire ground a cigarette under his mired boots: "Perhaps you did, monsieur. I don't know about such things. You say you climbed out of a grave. But, *nom de Dieu,* it didn't stay empty. You put my son in it." He glanced at Falk with a hint of satisfaction, like a player who has landed a difficult shot. He repeated the words savoring their astute propriety: *"Non monsieur,* it didn't stay empty very long, that fine grave of yours."

"I know," said Falk, "I killed your son in an act of futile reprisal, and in the hour of his victory. I found life in this house and brought death. You are right. Open graves gape until they are filled. That one should have had me in it." He said it with harsh finality, as if it was a lesson learnt long ago and implacably repeated. "I don't deny that for a moment. How could I?" Terrenoire watched from under his lids. He had seen larks fling themselves about thus before yielding to the net. "And I can't make it good to you, ever. There is no price on death."

"To be sure," said the old man, "those are the very words I used to Clotilde. He can't make up for Jean's death. They've paid the Ronquiers for the trees they sawed down, and more than they were worth, believe me. But they don't pay for the sons they killed. So I said to her: Monsieur Falk must have something else in mind." And again he blinked with an air of patient complicity.

"When I had to get out of here, the drums began all over again. I've told you what happened to me. But though I lived in hell and saw enough of horror each day to drive a man insane, it could no longer destroy me. Even at the worst, in Hamburg, after they dragged me away from the canal, and then in Leipzig when the Russians were upon us, I could shut my eyes for an instant and imagine myself back at La Hurlette. I swore that if that blue pitcher went unbroken so would I. Before decamping with my men, I buried it under a mound of hay in your barn. It must be there still. I should know if anything had happened to it; something inside me would have a crack. Because I had lived here, I knew that outside the world of the mad and the dead there was something else, something that might survive the war intact. I swore I would come back one day and hear the silence."

Terrenoire plucked a wet hair from the corner of his mouth: "That's very moving, Monsieur Falk, though I don't pretend to understand all of it. *Mais c'est gentil,* and I can see that a place like this would seem better than *Wehrmacht* barracks or the Russian front. But now you've come back and had a good look. Just like the Americans who come here every summer to show their families the beaches and the cemeteries. But I don't see you packing your suitcase. On the contrary, you seem to be settling in. *À quoi bon?* What do you really want from us?"

"I wasn't sure until I came back," said Falk, "I knew inside me all the time, but didn't dare think it through. Now I know, beyond any doubt. I am in love with Danielle. I have been the whole time. I want to marry her."

Terrenoire's face opened, startled and off guard. "You want to marry Danielle?" He was fending for time, like a clam burrowing.

"If she will have me."

"If she will have you? *Parbleu,* she's not the only one concerned. *Non, monsieur,* things are not that simple around here." He was on his own terrain now and confident. "You've killed my eldest son and want to marry my youngest daughter. *Drôle d'idée.* You Germans are deep ones, I'll say that for you." He laughed drily.

Falk made a tired, submissive gesture: "Five years are gone since that happened. It's unredeemable, I know. But Danielle and I are alive, and there can be children and new life here."

"No doubt," countered Terrenoire, "but there are many things to be thought of." Falk passed his hand over the bark of a young tree: "You are right, Monsieur Terrenoire. I don't even know whether Danielle will listen to me. I fear she will laugh in my face."

"Haven't you spoken to her yet?" "No," said Falk. A glint of malice lit in Terrenoire's pupils: "But you have spoken to Nicole?" Falk was silent. "That was stupid of you, Monsieur Falk. You Germans have no finesse, for all your lofty ideas." The two men had drifted to the edge of the sown field. The haystacks smoked slightly under the morning sun and to the left the ash tree cast its blue shadow. "But perhaps you were right after all," said Terrenoire: "This matter really concerns Nicole." He cracked his knuckles: *"Dans mon pays,* monsieur, we don't marry off our younger daughters before their older sisters are settled. *Et voilà."*

Both the force and the irrelevance of the argument struck Falk. Even as he answered, pleading that there must be exceptions to such rules, his own words seemed to him feeble and wide of the mark. Terrenoire did not bother to refute him, but pressed forward: "Nicole will make you a good wife. She's a little dry, *un peu sec,* like her mother, but a solid girl. She enjoys putting her nose in books, like you do, Monsieur Falk. She won't give you any trouble." He warmed to his theme: "You may have got hold of something with all your fine talk. You can't replace Jean on the farm with that leg of yours, but you can make a proper home for Nicole and help us out a bit. That's some return for what we had to put up with."

Falk intruded vehemently. There could be no question of marriage between himself and Mademoiselle Nicole, though he was fond and admiring of her. He was in love with Danielle. That she was the younger sister was awkward, he granted, but it couldn't be helped. If Danielle would not have him, he would leave at once and the Terrenoires would see no further trace of him. *"Merde,"* said the old man, "Danielle is much too young for you. I won't allow it. She's too young."

"I am ten years older than she is. But we're exactly the same age. We've seen and endured the same things. Outside Odessa we rounded up a group of partisans and made ready to hang them. Among them there was a Jewish boy. I couldn't believe that he was a day over fifteen. I asked him. He answered: 'I am fifteen add a thousand. To get a Jew's proper age, you should always add a thousand.' It's like that with the whole lot of us. For those who lived in the war, ten years' difference hardly matters. We carry the same mark."

Terrenoire broke off. Words were like pips in his mouth; he spat them out and was done with them. Shuffling back to the farmyard, he kept aloof from Falk's urgent plea. He stopped for a moment at the pigpen and clucked his tongue, loud as a pistol shot. The sow shifted her haunches in lazy recognition. Nearly at the threshold, Terrenoire turned bitterly: "Get one thing through your head, Monsieur Falk: if you marry Danielle, you won't get a penny out of me, *pas un liard.* I'll put her out like a beggar. With Nicole it might be different. I don't say I could give you much. You and your friends saw to that. But Nicole is the oldest. She wouldn't leave my house empty-handed."

"I don't expect anything," said Falk. "That has never entered my mind. On the contrary." Terrenoire looked up. "I have put some money aside. I am an electrical engineer. I'm partner in a small business in Hanover. We are well on our feet. On the contrary, Monsieur Terrenoire, it is I . . ."

They entered the kitchen. Madame Terrenoire was scraping carrots over a cracked bowl. "You'll never guess," said Terrenoire with a watery smile, "Monsieur Falk has not come back to buy apples or see the landscape. *Il est prétendant, parbleu;* he is a suitor." She said nothing, but her hands ceased from their quick labor.

*

Falk found no immediate occasion to press his suit. Danielle had left for Harfleur, where her aunt kept a draper's shop. Falk remembered the little lady, hewn like a benevolent gargoyle of out a pink, brittle stone. Tante Amélie lived in implacable detestation of the English; she regarded them as cunning wolves who had sought to ruin France either by direct incursion or by entangling her in bloody wars for their own secret vantage. Forced to leave her home when the old port had been turned into a German bastion, Amélie had gone to live with a bachelor cousin in Angers. She had passed through La Hurlette, giving away bales of cloth and her stock of ribbons lest they fall into English hands. She had welcomed Falk as an ally brought into France by harsh but provident destiny. When she chronicled for him the numerous occasions on which the English had sacked Harfleur, the antique conflagrations seemed to burn in her high cheeks.

Danielle often went over to Harfleur to spend a day in the musty shop, passing her fingers over the raw linen and *crêpes de chine*. Nicole told Falk in a dead voice that her sister was coming home by the late afternoon bus. He went to Yvebecques to meet her.

Watching Danielle step off the bus, Falk experienced a sense of painful unreality. He had rehearsed the scene too often in his imagination, first in the prisoner-of-war camp at Dortmund, and later in Hanover when trying to salvage life out of the rubble. Now the girl came toward him as in a worn, abstract remembrance. Even the excitement that rose in him was stale. And because he was numb and momentarily remote, Falk saw Danielle as she really was, not as he had obstinately dreamt her.

She had grown straight but her body had not filled out. It was full of hollows and awkward movement. Only her face had taken on a broad strength. The large gray eyes and steady mouth gave it an alert, nearly masculine beauty, but one could discern flat bones under the skin. Danielle would take after her mother, and Falk glimpsed, beneath the nearing girl, the later woman, secretive and perhaps a little coarse.

In an instant, however, he could no longer see her as someone apart from himself. Crossing the market place and entering the Rue de la Poissonnière, she had passed completely into the troubled light of his desire.

Seeing Falk, Danielle gave a small, abrupt nod, as if to say, 'I knew you would be here. I have been thinking about it on the bus, all the way from Harfleur'; but neither spoke. She came near and suddenly put her hand out as adversaries do before a match. Unready, Falk did not meet her gesture and their hands fumbled. At this they laughed, the strain holding them close. She began walking beside him, slowing her step to his labored progress.

They said nothing until the road started climbing away from the village. But Falk could not keep his glance from her hair. The blood ached in his temples. When Danielle spoke, it was as if their thoughts had already conversed in intimate dispute. "Are there no girls left in Germany, Monsieur Falk?" He started. "That's what I said to Tante Amélie. Poor Monsieur Falk. There are no girls left in Germany. *Pas une seule.* So he had to pack his suitcase and come all the way to Yvebecques to find one."

"And what did your aunt say to that?"

"She told me not to worry my head about such matters but to thank *la bonne Vierge Marie* that you had come back. Tante Amélie is very taken with you, you know. You should visit her in Harfleur."

"I hope to," said Falk.

"Yes, she's still hoping that you will defeat the English. You've let her down badly."

"I'm afraid we'll have to explain to her that it didn't work out that way."

"It didn't, did it?" said Danielle lightly.

"No. But that's over and done with. It happened a long time ago."

"A long time?" she echoed him as from a far dimness.

"Yes, longer than we need remember. Believe me, Danielle."

"I thought so too. Until you walked back into our kitchen the other night. When I saw you again I heard the ash tree creaking. I had not heard it creak that way since the winter after you left. And when I ran past you I went into the garden. The bark is still worn where the rope was."

"No. That's not true. The bark has renewed itself and the branch has grown."

"That would be too simple," said Danielle.

Falk blazed up as if she had touched the very nerve of him. "Simple? On the contrary. It is much simpler to stiffen in silence or hate. Hate keeps warm. That's child's play. It would have been much simpler for me to die in Hamburg near the canal. Or to stay in Hanover and marry a widow with a pension and cast the image of you out of my mind. Do you think it's easy to come back here? In Germany we don't talk about the past. We all have amnesia or perhaps someone put an iron collar around our necks so that we can't look back. That's one way of doing it. Then there's the other, the unrelenting way. Steep yourself in the remembered horrors. Build them around you like a high safe wall. Is that any less easy or dishonest?"

She lashed out: "God knows I wish the past didn't exist! I didn't ask for those memories, did I? You forced them down our throats, the whole savage pack of you! And now you come and tell us we should forget and live for the future. You're spitting on graves. The dead will start howling when you pass."

She broke off; there were tears of rage in her voice. Had Falk not grasped her arm she would have darted ahead. But he held her rooted. "Try and understand what I'm saying. I'm not asking you to forget anything. I want you to remember your brother, and, if you must, the burn of the rope on the branch. But remember Bültner also. Think of the apples he threw at you and think of him lying alive in the ditch when they came with their flails. And if you think of all the dead, of yours and of ours, it will become more bearable. I don't want you to forget. The stench of forgetting is so strong in Germany that I came back here to breath real air. But that's only the beginning, the easy part, like learning to walk again. They taught me that in the hospital. It hurt so much I kept passing out. But it was really very simple. It's after you've learnt to walk that the terrible part begins. Suddenly you discover that you have to go some place."

"I don't want to go. I want to be left alone." And she drew away into the evening shadows.

When Falk caught up with her, lights were coming on in the village. On the horizon a tanker moved like a black thread across the molten wake of the sun. The air was still with the first touch of night.

Danielle turned to him: "Nicole is in love with you." She said it with the solemn malice of a child.

"Don't mock me."

"No. It's true. We used to quarrel about you when we were girls. We knew how handsome you were but pretended you wore a mask and vied with one another in describing how fearful you would look without it. She said she couldn't stand you because you were nasty and conceited and gave yourself airs like an old rooster. I was silly in those days and believed her. But after you left she went gray inside. She never found anyone else. When she turned down Jacques Estève—his people own the dairy on the road to Fécamp—I ran after him and told him to chop off one of his legs. He thought I was mad. If *la Sainte Vierge* has brought you back here, it's for Nicole's sake. She will make you happy. *Elle sera bonne pour vous.* She's clever and serious. She knows ever so much more than I do. She can understand your books and the long words you use. And I would be your sister-in-law. Then we could sit by the chimney and talk about your children."

Involuntarily, Falk took up her tone: "And what about your children, *belle-soeur?*"

"Mine? Ah, the little horrors! Jean—he's the oldest one, you know—will always be in trouble. They'll send him home from school for putting girls' pigtails in the inkwell and for writing wicked things on the walls. So I shall have to be very angry with him. I shall pack him off to Germany to work in his uncle's factory. You will have a factory, won't you? And you will tell me how he's getting on and see to it that he writes his *maman*. And when he comes home I shall be proud of him, and he will have learned to be an engineer like you."

In the pending darkness Danielle seemed to discern the shapes of her invention. She moved after them: "And there will be many

daughters. Four at least. They will have long red hair and blue
eyes, not gray like mine. I shall have to go to Rouen and Le
Havre to find husbands for them. They will be so pert that no
one will want them."

"And what will you do then?"

"I shall send them to you and ask you to put them in a nun-
nery deep in the Black Forest! Tell me, is it really black?"

"Yes."

"They won't like that. They will drape their red hair out the
window until someone rescues them and there will be a mighty
scandal. So I shall have to bring them home and build them a
house up on the *grande falaise*. There they will sit and stick their
tongues out at passers-by and grow into spinsters like four tall
candles."

"Will you visit them?"

"From time to time. When the wind is high. And we will
gather at the fire to talk about the past."

"What will you tell them of the past?"

Danielle wavered and then bent near; "That it was long ago."

Falk found her clasped hands. He opened them gently. But
beneath his soft motion she felt the surge of longing, watchful
and implacable. It filled her with strange anguish, as if the entire weight of the night was upon her. She drew back rebellious:
"Look," she cried out; "look!"

Falk turned heavily. Banks of clouds had mounted in the
northern sky. But here and there they were thinning out; behind
them shimmered a vague white line. "England," she said; "those
are the English cliffs."

"I don't think so," said Falk trying to keep the edge out of his
voice; "it's probably moonlight reflecting on the clouds. You
rarely see the English coast from here. Even with our glasses it
was difficult to tell whether we were seeing cliffs or a trick of
light."

"I remember your glasses," said Danielle quickly, "in their big
leather case. Do you still have them?"

"No, I sold them to an American soldier for a tin of coffee.
What else do you remember?"

"Everything. The smell of your coat and the loose strap on

your helmet and the way you kept forgetting your furred gloves in the kitchen. And I remember the time after you left. I tried to hate you. With every nerve inside me. I kept my eyes tight shut so that I could see before me Jean's body and the bit of rope your men left on the ash tree. But I didn't succeed. That was what made me ill. I couldn't hate you. I didn't know how." But even as she said it the weight of his presence enveloped her and she fought against it: "You see, Monsieur Falk, I am a silly girl. I don't know much about hatred and I don't know about love. *Je suis bonne à rien.*" She laughed as if she had sprung free from his reach.

"Have you never been in love, Danielle?"

"Oh, many times!"

"Seriously?"

The hurt in his voice provoked her: "Desperately. With Siccard at the florist's. With Monsieur Lurôt's cousin who lives in Rouen and owns two silk waistcoats. With Fridolin. He drives a green truck and takes me for rides in it."

"And now?"

The lightness drained away; something urgent and wearing rose at her. She sought to force it down. She liked to tear green currants off the bush and put them between her teeth. It was the same bitter, exciting taste. Falk asked again, "And now?"

"I don't know. I don't know."

They had not taken the straight way to La Hurlette but had strayed on to a small path which led to the rim of the cliff. There it plunged sharply down the face, ending in a niche dug out of the rock. Just large enough for two men, the hollow had served as a machine-gun nest. Looming from the dirt parapet, the barrel had a cruel sweep of the bay. Below it the cliff fell sheer into the sea. Like a gannet's eyrie, the narrow platform hung suspended between the dark folds of the rock and the clamor of the water. Falk had often gone there to inspect the watch, to inhale the salt rush of night or peer at the red flashes on the English coast. One had to speak loud to make oneself heard above the seethe and bellow of the waves. During the March storms, spray had been known to leap skyward, sending a plume of cold white mist over the huddled gunners. But on summer nights, at the recession of the tide, there were moments of near silence, with the sea running far below, the foam driven on it like white leaves.

Falk held Danielle close: "I love you, I love you." The words seemed arrogant and trivial in the indifference of the night. But he went on heedless: "I am not bringing you very much. This carcass of mine and half a wedding present. The other half is lying in the gutter in the Rue de la Poissonnière. Let's leave it there. Half may be enough. I don't want to ask for the whole of life any more. Only for you, and for time enough to quarrel and make children and grow old together. If I have to, I'll even take those four wicked daughters into the bargain. It's a bad bargain, Danielle, I know that. The merchandise has been damaged in transit. God knows you could do better. There must be fine young men about, with fine legs. Of your own people. Not the enemy, not the *sale boche.* There may be some around who could love you more blindly than I do. They wouldn't notice that your nose has grown a little too long. They might even make you happier than I can. But I won't let them have you. I want you. Utterly for myself. You cannot conceive how selfish I have grown. I believe with all my soul that I will make you happy. But I don't know whether that counts most. All I do know, all I care for, is that you are life to me, all of it I can grasp or make sense of now. I was a dead man when I first saw you, when you walked into my room that night. I breathed you in like air and began living. The presence of you inside me has kept me alive since. I love you, Danielle, selfishly and desperately. I cannot take no for an answer."

The vehemence of it held her rigid. But though she was afraid and uncertain, a bright malice flashed through her. "Say it in German," she demanded; "say it in German."

"*Ich liebe dich*, Danielle."

She shaped the words awkwardly for herself: "*Ich liebe dich.*" They stuck in her teeth like a bitter rind. "It's not very beautiful that way. *Je vous aime* is better." She felt the tightness and impatience in his grip. "You are hurting me. Let go."

He did, and she swayed against the sudden gulf of night. "*Ich liebe dich.*" She tried again and could not suppress an abrupt, unreasoned gaiety. "I would be Madame Falk. How strange. *Bon-*

soir, Madame Falk."

"Danielle, come back to me. Come into my room, as you always did, with the morning sun. Put your hand on my sleeve. Tell me that you know what I'm asking for. That you love me."

She turned and took his head between her hands, staring at him for an instant as if he was a stranger; then she drew him down swiftly. They stood gathered to each other. Even now, unsteady with delight and a great tiredness, Falk urged once more: "Tell me." He heard the words from a sudden closeness: *"Je vous aime."*

At the foot of the cliffs the sea was beginning to simmer. They drew in the roused air and the salt lay sharp on their tongues. Holding Danielle fast, Falk told her of the blue pitcher. At first she did not remember. And when he told her of how he had buried it in the barn and of what it signified to him during the last months of war, rebellion stung her. He had planned it all. She had no existence of her own. She was part of a stubborn dream. She swerved back like a small angry flame: "I can't understand why you make so much of it. It was a cheap little jug. We never used the good china for our guests." She gave the word a fine edge of scorn.

But he seemed beyond her reach and she followed mutinous yet entranced as they clambered back up the cliff and struck out for La Hurlette.

"We must go to the barn, Danielle, and dig it up. I know we shall find it unbroken. I did not dare look before. Now I know. My love. My love." And he clasped her tight as they hurried through the trees.

Joined to his lunging step, Danielle felt herself in Falk's power. It gave her insidious content, as if she had been a swimmer who stops thrashing and yields to the seaward drag of the tide. But she could not let go entirely. The precariousness of their condition was too vivid in her mind. Too much of what lay before them was unanswered.

"Falk."

"Yes?"

"Even if it's true what we said back there, even if we are in love . . ."

"Yes, Danielle?"

"What can come of it, Falk? They won't let us marry."

"Why not?"

"Because you're not one of us, and they look on me as a child. And it would do Nicole dreadful hurt."

"None of that concerns us, Danielle. Not really. I know it's true, but it can't be helped, and does it matter?"

"I don't think I would like to come with you to Germany. No. I don't think I would want to leave here. You mustn't ask it of me."

"Perhaps I will have to. And much more. Love is asking. All the time. For more than anyone ever dreamt of giving."

"I don't have that much to give, Falk."

"What there is I will take! Be warned."

She caught the lightness in his tone but also the obstinate desire. In the dark of the hedgerows his step seemed surer than hers.

"I'm afraid, Falk. I'm afraid."

"Of what?"

"I don't know. Of what they'll say in the village. Of your German friends. Of Jean. I fear his ghost. It will seek us out. It will harrow our lives. Don't laugh at me. It's God's truth. He will find us and damn us to hell."

"I am not laughing, Danielle. Perhaps he will come. In some way I wish he would. It would make my happiness more bearable. If we receive him into our lives, he will forgive us. Ghosts are watchdogs and children must learn to live with them in the house. And learn their language. I have heard it. They speak like snow."

"Father won't give us anything. If we leave here, I shall have to go as a beggar." "I know," said Falk gaily; "Monsieur Terrenoire made that quite plain. And here I came all the way from Hanover just to snatch your dowry. Think of it!" His laughter rang out.

"Be serious, Falk. There is so much against us. We are mad to carry on this way."

"I love you, Danielle." His voice left her naked. "Don't you understand? I love you. Everything you say is true. We are sur-

rounded by absurd and hateful things. It will be even more difficult than you or I can imagine. Perhaps they will want to hang
me and shave your head." She felt his fingers pass through her
hair in rough solace. "I don't know whether I must go back to
Hanover or whether we can live in France. But does it matter?
I love you. And if I said it over and over all night long you
wouldn't have heard the beginning of it!"

They moved in silence. Then Falk resumed. "You have a beautiful name. I will often call you in our house, not because I shall
need anything, but to say it. Danielle. It's like a cool bright stone
that has lain in a mountain stream."

"Please, stop it Falk. I can't bear it. I'm too afraid."

They were nearly at La Hurlette. Falk entered the barn and
advanced through the warm blackness with the surety of a blind
man. Danielle saw him kneel in one of the old stalls now empty
of horses. He scattered the crackling hay and the trodden dirt.
Then he pried loose one of the floorboards and she heard the
nails scrape. Suddenly he paused and she caught the tense pleasure in his voice. "Danielle, come here!" Once again she felt as if
she had become a shadow to his being. She stepped nearer. "I
have it. It's here. Exactly as I buried it." The object tinkled
faintly as if the lid was loose. Falk brushed the dirt away cra-
dling the little pitcher against his body. Then he rose trium-
phant. "It's unbroken, Danielle. It's been waiting for us all these
years. My love, it's unbroken. Feel the edge. Not a chip. Take it.
We shall drink from it in the mornings. Just as we used to."

He was reaching toward her when the beam of light struck
between them. The pitcher shone blue, and abrupt shadows
sprang up the wall. Blaise was standing in the doorway, the lamp
held stiffly before him. Danielle grasped the pitcher and bent
away. The cows shifted in the hot still air.

Blaise strode in, breathing heavily. He rapped the girl across
the mouth with the back of his hand, not in fury but bewildered
scorn: *"Petite putain."*

Falk strained toward her but Blaise barred his way. He stood
like a circus trainer, his powerful legs straddled: "I'm fed up.
J'en ai marre. You're getting out of here. Tonight. You've made
enough trouble. You're going to leave us in peace. We don't want

you around here. Never again. I'm warning you. Get out while you can." He talked low but his features were convulsed with hatred.

Falk flung out into the dark: "Danielle, tell him we love each other. Tell him we're leaving together."

"If she makes a move," said Blaise, "I'll beat the daylights out of her. But she won't move. She's just a stupid little goose. You may have turned her head with your fancy speeches. But she's coming to her senses. Look at her." He swept the light across her inert face.

"Danielle, tell him the truth. Come with me." She was staring at Falk but not seeing him. "For God's sake, Danielle, rouse yourself! Remember all that we've said, all that's happened. If I go now without you, I can never return." But she lifted her hands to her face and shrank from the light.

"Enough of this farce," said Blaise. "Get out of here. You can wait in the village. There's a bus to Rouen at daybreak. Get going, *mon capitaine*."

"Let me through to her," demanded Falk. "She's frightened of you. You're an ugly brute. But she loves me. Do you hear? She loves me! And nothing you can do will change that."

Blaise grinned. He knew his ground. When he turned to Danielle it was as if he had flicked a restive calf across the nose. "Why don't you say something to the handsome gentleman? He's waiting." He kept the lamp on her.

"Please," she moaned, "leave me alone. It's no good. They'll kill you if you stay. I told you it wouldn't do any good. You must go."

"Come with me," cried Falk.

"I can't. I don't dare. Perhaps I don't love you enough. Please let me be. Please." She kept her hands before her eyes, against Falk's anguish and the unswerving light.

Falk raised his cane but Blaise tore it from his grasp easily: "I could hammer your brains out right now. No one would care. But why bother? You're going to leave just like you came. Like a lame dog." He snapped the cane across his leg and threw the pieces into a mound of hay.

As he hobbled out of the barn, his hands clutching for support,

Falk caught a last glimpse of Danielle. She had turned to the wall.

*

When she set out in pursuit of Falk late the next morning, Danielle was like a creature possessed. Only moments after he had been driven from the barn, a sense of utter desolation assailed her. She had run through the courtyard calling Falk's name under her breath. But darkness had swallowed him. She knew with the blinding certainty of pain that she could not endure without him. Her love was not the unbewildered glory he had demanded, but though imperfect, it made up the sum of life. Having come moments too late, this knowledge mocked her. The remembrance of her evasion and of Falk's crippled departure under the derisive flourish of Blaise's lamp, made her skin tight and cold. It was like a palpable nightmare and she could not shake it off.

Loathing herself, she stood under the chill heavy rain which began toward midnight as if it could scour her clean. Danielle watched from the arcade of the market hall as the dawn bus left for Rouen, but there was no sign of Falk. She hastened along the top of the cliff and stared vaguely at the woken sea. Then back to La Hurlette. She put on dry clothes and started out again, brushing Nicole aside as if she were an intruder.

As she hurried back to the village, the whole landscape turned to bleak unreality. The thought of not seeing Falk again filled her with wild misery. Yet she was afraid of meeting him. He would not forgive her cowardice and giddiness of mind. He knew her now for a shallow girl. He had said he would never come back.

Danielle began whimpering like a child. When she had been very little, she had been banished to her room for snatching rowdily at a sweet bun. After a time her father had come to the door. She could have her brioche if only she would express remorse for her wicked manners. Fighting back tears, Danielle had refused. On his way downstairs, Terrenoire casually popped the bun into his own mouth. Seeing it vanish, Danielle had felt the

world collapse. She had howled with rage and sorrow. Now the
same feeling of absurd deprivation engulfed her. She had thrown
away her life in frivolous unknowing.

Ferreting about in Yvebecques, she found news. Between gulps
of coffee Pervienne told her that when crossing his field, just after
daybreak, he had seen a man hobbling down the road. He was
leaning on what looked like a large dead branch. After a while
the man had flagged down a truck and Pervienne had watched
him clamber on to the back amid crates of lettuce and cabbage.
Pervienne had an orderly mind. Wiping the last drop of coffee
from the rim of the cup, he recalled that the truck bore the blue-
and-yellow markings of the *Union agricole*. Doubtless it was on
the way to Le Havre.

Only later, when the bus was actually entering the suburbs, did
Danielle realize the futility of her search. The raids had torn
great gashes in the city. Blocks of new, raw houses stood between
stretches of vacant terrain. On the mounds of rubble the grass
had a metallic sheen. The dust and clamor of construction lay
thick in the air. As she hurried over upchurned roads, seeking
out the garage of the *Union*, Danielle saw high cranes swing
stiffly across the sky.

The garage was a cavernous hangar. Naked light bulbs threw
a cold glare. In the far recesses the trucks stood hunched and silent. The dispatcher and the drivers were lounging in a small
shed. Danielle rapped several times on the murky panes before
they took notice. When they opened the door she smelled kero-
sene and wet leather. She asked whether any of them had seen
a lame man; one of their trucks had given him a lift from Yvebecques. He had been hobbling on a dead branch. Did anyone remember him, and where had they dropped him off in Le Havre?

The drivers looked at her and she drew her raincoat tighter.
They told her to come in and get dry. The dispatcher rolled a
cigarette and held it out. But she hung at the door asking obstinately. The man was very lame. He had red hair. Did no one
remember? The drivers shrugged and glanced at each other.
Finally one of them spoke up from the back of the shed. It was
against company rules. But *merde,* the man could hardly walk
and was worn out. So he had let him ride on the crates and when

the rain had thickened had given him a sheet of burlap to burrow under. The dispatcher remarked sourly that the *Union
agricole* was no bus line. Danielle asked: where had the man
seen set down? "I told him I could not be seen with a passenger
near the garage," answered the driver, "so I dropped him off
Boulevard Galliéni. There's a bakery on the corner. I saw him
enter there."

A young trucker with blotches on his chin called out to Danielle: "Little lady, is he your lover?" "Yes," she said and hurried
out of the garage.

One of the girls at the bakery remembered Falk. He had eaten
several rolls standing at the counter. He had seemed ravenous
and his clothes were sodden. He had left a puddle on the floor.
The owner looked up from the apricot tarts and gave Danielle a
sullen stare. Did anyone notice where he was heading? The girls
giggled. Why should they?

During the ensuing hours Danielle wandered the city, now
with directed intent, now in random circles, up and down the
dust-blown boulevards, through the scarred streets, past the
wharfs and corrugated-iron sheds, between warehouses and gan-
tries, pausing in brief stupor on the freshly painted benches in
the new playgrounds, and then hurrying on through the blind
drifts of the afternoon crowd to the bus terminal and the railway
station. She peered into *brasseries,* empty cafés and restaurants,
treading the mill of the long day in a torment of loss and weari-
ness.

A hundred times in the drag of hours Danielle saw Falk just
ahead of her and ran toward him only to find a stranger in her
path. His face and harried step seemed to leap at her out of the
crowd; she saw it mirrored in the glass alembics in apothecary
windows. Soon the city flickered in her sore eyes like the reels of
a blurred film. Streets, building sites and quays revolved around
her in a lazy, jeering motion, always the same, yet malignantly
altered so that she could not be sure that she had already
searched them out.

Looking up at the cranes, Danielle prayed for the miracle of
momentary flight, imagining herself gyrating over the sea of roofs
and streets, able to discern Falk and plummet upon him. Instead

she plodded interminably and evening crowded at her with its delusive shadows.

She had tried to swallow a sandwich earlier in the day but it had gone stale in her mouth. Now a soft, sour nausea stirred in her throat. She sat on a fallen oil barrel and started at the graying harbor. The rust flaked between her fingers, but she kept a stubborn grip and fought off dizziness. Suddenly she lowered her head and vomited. A great lightness overcame her and she felt a pang of hope.

Once again Danielle crossed the Boulevard Galliéni and circled the Place de la Libération. Hunger made her alert and quick. It rang in her head like a small chime. She began counting lampposts: "At the sixteenth I shall find Falk." And when the sixteenth had passed, she started over again with the same spurt of hope.

But after a time she stopped counting and began weeping helplessly. Despair stole on her as out of ambush. She had consumed the last of herself. The wine was spilt and she tasted the dregs and lees of her own being.

When she saw Falk she could no longer muster even joy. He was standing on a small wharf looking at the oil-flecked water. He was leaning on an umbrella. Despite its massive old-fashioned handle, it had already bent under his weight. Danielle called to him in a dead voice. It did not carry and she sickened at the thought that he would turn away. She called again and stretched her hands toward him. He looked about and grew white as if he had seen that which was crying out in the midst and secret of his soul gather shape in the evening air.

As they left the wharf, neither spoke. Only their fingers touched. They drank coffee in silence and looked in bewilderment at their own image in the misted silver urn. They said nothing to each other as they followed the *portier* up the stairs of the hotel. Falk's umbrella tapped on the worn tiles.

The shutters were closed but from the streetlights jagged shapes fell across the brown wallpaper and enamel basin. They sat in the musty quiet hearing the noise of day ebb from the city. At last Falk wrenched open the wooden blinds.

Searchlights were sweeping across the harbor like blue danc-

ers. As Falk stepped back into the room Danielle rose. She guided his hands. Together they undid the buttons on her dress. The
siren of a liner was singing westward. At first brazen and clear,.
then softly as if the sound had run into the sands of night.

*

The day of the wedding was unusually warm. The stone beach;
merged into banks of white haze. The first brown spots were ap-
pearing in the hedgerows, leaves burnt by the departing summer.
The Terrenoires had assembled in the garden. Each had yielded
in his own fashion. The old man had voiced muted approval:
Ce n'est pas une mauvaise affaire. Madame Terrenoire had;
scarcely said anything. Events had come to pass as she foretold.
She saw in the tumult and brusque conclusion of Falk's court-
ship proof of her divining powers. She kept the silence of an
oracle and spent more time than she used to with Nicole. There
was between them the unspoken discourse of conspirators. Both
were old women now, gazing ahead to the bland pleasures of a
common winter. To Danielle and Falk, Nicole had come hand-
somely, wishing them Godspeed and seeking to make her presence no attainder to their joy.

Only Blaise was absent. He had shrugged off Falk's attempt at
conciliation and had thrust his hands in his pocket. The day before the wedding he took his bicycle from the shed and said terse-
ly that he was off to the market at Coutances.

Tante Amélie had come over from Harfleur. She was whir-
ring about like a drunken bee when smoke has routed it from its
hive. She scattered loud delight and the hem of her mauve dress
billowed along the ground. At every instant she would clasp
either bride or bridegroom to the large cameo brooch on her
bosom. Her warm cheeks were streaked with tears. The dreary
war had not been in vain. All had come well in the end. Tante
Amélie had stitched a pale yellow gown for Danielle and presented Falk with a plum-colored waistcoat. Now she darted about
dusting off everyone in a whirl of order. Suddenly she peered at
her pendant watch and sang out: *"Allons, enfants!"*

The party advanced through the orchard. They moved stiffly

under the apple boughs, the women ample and flowery, the two men like sable penguins.

A few villagers were waiting in the silent chamber of the *mairie*. No one had taken the dustcover from the chandelier. Monsieur Raymond, the mayor, was a spare, sallow man; but even he was perspiring. Having donned his tricolor sash, he read out the marriage service in a low, precise intonation. Danielle strained forward as if the gray words were of passionate interest. Falk's eyes wandered to the wall. From behind a dusty glass the General looked stonily on the proceedings. For a brief second Falk panicked. He could remember no French. But then he heard his own voice. Danielle assented in a whisper. Her lips were ash-dry, but as she embraced Falk, Tante Amélie vented a loud sob and Danielle began smiling.

Monsieur Raymond took off his glasses, wiped the moisture from the bridge of his nose and addressed the young couple. It was, he felt, an unusual, indeed, a portentous occasion. He would be doing less than his sworn duty if he did not call the attention of the newlyweds, of their family and friends, to the significance of the event. The Terrenoires had lived in Yvebecques longer than records showed. Monsieur Beltran, the clerk—*ce véritable savant*—affirmed that there were Terrenoires baptized and buried in the village in the seventeenth century. Monsieur Falk belonged to another world. He had come (here the mayor paused) in a manner—how should one say?—not altogether natural or beneficent. But Yvebecques had proved stronger than tragic circumstances. Its style of life, its renowned natural beauties, had entered into Monsieur Falk's heart. He had come back "over the hidden but unerring road of love." The mayor allowed the sentence to unfurl in the hushed room and looked at the ceiling. Might there not be in this, he asked, a lesson for the weary and divided nations? Here, in the *mairie* of Yvebecques, *notre petit village*, two young people had achieved what the captains of the earth sought vainly. "Yet, would Monsieur Falk forgive me if I add one further thought to this joyous hour? Even now and in this blessed moment, one should not forget the past. Like so many other families in the community, the Terrenoires bear witness in their bone and blood to the sufferings of France. *La patrie* had not wished for war, but thrice it assailed her. May this marriage be a portent of a more felicitous future. But may it also keep us in solemn remembrance of what has been endured."

Amélie sobbed again and Monsieur Cavel, the aged clerk, blew his nose. The mayor congratulated the happy couple and everyone filed into the open air. But no breeze stirred. Passing the fountain, Falk shifted his new lacquered cane and dipped his fingers in the water. He touched Danielle's lips. She nibbled the cold drops and the flush of desire that spread through her limbs was so strong that she leaned heavily against Falk's arm. The wedding party entered the café.

When they started out again for La Hurlette, the awkward silences had melted. The small glasses of tart red wine and the apéritifs were busy in the blood. Joined by further guests, the procession straggled through the village and toward the cliff. The gentlemen loosened their collars and tilted their straw hats against the veiled, relentless sun. The ladies advanced slowly, prickly and pouting for air. They called to one another; in the heat their voices crackled like dry grass. Danielle and Falk moved a little to one side. She sucked the moisture from her lips and kept her eyes to the ground as if seeking coolness in her own scant shadow. Falk felt sweat pearling down his collar and back: it chilled him. Beating against the chalk cliff, the air simmered. The birds had fallen silent, but among the hedges and wilted stalks wasps sung with a hum of low flame.

"I've lived here sixty-four years," panted Monsieur Cavel, "and never been so hot."

"It is unusual," allowed the mayor; "most unusual."

"One might as well be in the Sahara," said Siccard, combing back his flaxen hair, "I've been there, and believe me, it was no hotter."

"Ah, the Sahara," said Monsieur Cavel.

Estève, who was now married and putting on weight, stopped and stared at the banks of haze drifting along the cliffs and over the soundless sea. "*Ça va barder,*" he announced; "there's bound to be one devil of a storm before the day is out."

"I hope so," said Nicole; "I'm stifling."

But Fridolin, who was bringing up the rear in a white linen suit, muttered "Storms on a wedding night. A bad omen."

"*They* won't hear it," said Estève, trying to look roguish.

But no one responded or came fully to life until Tante Amélie called out: "*Courage, mes enfants,* we're nearly there."

The orchard was not much cooler, as if the sun had seeped into the shadows. Madame Terrenoire paused to tug at her corset. The men wiped the sweat from their faces and Monsieur Raymond closed his collar button. Nicole bore in on the newlyweds: "You must take the lead now." The smile on her lips was taut as in a bad photograph. Falk led Danielle to the gate and the mayor began clapping. Others joined, but in the stifling air the sound fell flat.

Everyone hurried under the trees and Amélie came into the garden carrying jugs of cider frosted at the rim. Siccard bellowed with pleasure. He raised his glass to bride and bridegroom, emptying it at one draught; the iced cider stunned him and his eyes blinked stupidly. The ladies drank with quick delicate sips and vanished into the house. Falk and Daniele drifted toward the shade of the barn. "I love you, Danielle." She did not answer but passed her fingers across his face in strangeness and wonder. They heard the clatter of dishes and the voices now more strident. Slowly they walked back to the long tables.

The food lay in garish heaps: bowls of dark blue mussels, steaming in milk; brick-red lobsters; fried mackerel bedded on ferns; plates of shrimp beside saucers of melted butter; larks, charred and spiky, cracking under one's teeth with a savor of game; two sides of beef sweating blood; tureens of fluffy white potatoes with warm napkins over them; watery endives; three cavernous bowls of dark green salad, shimmering with oil and nuggets of black pepper. Between the laden galleons, small boats and barks brimmed with spices, shelled walnuts and dried fruit. Long loaves were aligned on the sideboards next to squares of fresh butter, cold from the larder. There were wine and cider glasses before each plate, but soon the guests filled them indiscriminately.

A hot, ruttish wind blew across the tables. Terrenoire had scarcely tied the checkered napkin around his chin before thrust-

ing his knife into a gamy paté and spreading it thick on a slab
of bread. Then he drew toward himself a mound of shrimp.
What had survived of lust in him was gluttony. Everyone followed suit. Cavel stuffed a lark into his toothless mouth and spat
out the fine bones amid a howl of laughter. Madame Estève, a
flushed stout woman with yellow eyes, carried the mussels to her
lips, sucking them loudly. Melted butter dribbled down the
mayor's chin as he leaned across the table. Fridolin carved the
beef with wide flourishes and licked the gravy off his fingers.
Monsieur Beltran had followed the main party after setting his
wax seal to the marriage certificate; now he shoveled food into
his gullet like a squirrel. He was the first to undo his braces.
Other gentlemen did likewise and Madame Estève squealed hap-
pily as Cavel unhooked her dress. Danielle and Falk ate little.

Legs rubbed drowsily under the table and the wine grew warm
in the uncorked bottles. Nicole could hardly keep up with the
empty glasses and her skin glistened. Fridolin wavered to his feet;
the wine was toiling in his brain and he moved his hands before
his face as if he had walked into a cobweb. He ambled to Danielle and bent low, staring down her dress. *"Mon poulet,* let me
tell you a thing or two about marriage. I am an experienced
man." She felt his loud, liquorish breath at her ear. The mayor
got slowly to his feet, sought to brush the crumbs and drippings
from his rumpled shirt front and proposed the health of Monsieur and Madame Falk.

The day was wilting: early shadows drifted through the vibrant air. Toast followed on toast. The surfeited guests roused
themselves as Madame Terrenoire and Tante Amélie brought in
platters of pancakes filled with raspberry jam. The black, sweet
jam was full of seeds and Siccard spat them through his teeth,
now at the mayor, now at Nicole. She set down small glasses on
the crowded tables and the *calvados* went from hand to hand.
Under the blazing rush of the liqueur nearly everyone stopped
eating. Only Terrenoire persisted, using his fork to snatch cold
leavings as Nicole began carrying the plates back to the kitchen.
Above the chaos of voices and clinking glass, Monsieur Raymond
called for a word from the groom.

Falk pushed the dishes away from in front of him and rose,

bracing his arms stiffly on the table. He looked down at Danielle
and was startled to see her so withdrawn. He expressed his delight at the festive occasion and thanked all the distinguished
guests for their presence. He raised his glass to Madame Terrenoire, to Nicole and to Tante Amélie, who had labored to provide this noble feast. Cavel fluttered his spoon against a de-
canter. But Falk could not sustain the mock ceremonious note.
He turned to the mayor: "Perhaps it would not be out of place,
Monsieur le Maire, if I responded more particularly to your own
eloquent words." Monsieur Raymond, who was trying to scrape
a clot of jam from his trousers, looked up blear-eyed.

"When I came back to Yvebecques, I was conscious of being
a most unwelcome intruder. That is the burden we Germans
must carry all over the world just now. And for a long time to
come our children will have to carry it, though they had no part
in our calamities. I have not tried to shed the load. I do not want
to. But henceforth Danielle will help me to carry it and that is
a kind of miracle." His hand rested momentarily on her shoulder. "I do not know yet where we shall make our home. But your
village, Monsieur Raymond, will always be as close to me as it
is to my wife."

Ma femme: it was the first time he used the word. It made
him light of heart as if in victory. "Here in this garden," he went
on; "here . . ."

"Under the ash tree, under the ash tree!" The voice stabbed
at Falk exact and derisive. Blaise was hovering near the pigsty.
With him were Lurôt and a coil of young men and women from
the neighboring farms. The voice sang out again like a javelin:
"Under the ash tree. That's where you want to make your home,
isn't it, *Herr Kapitän!*"

Falk sat down heavily. But the guests neither understood nor
cared. They thumped the tables and called raucously to the new
arrivals. Estève staggered over to Blaise with a glass of *calvados*.
He lurched into one of the farm girls and spilled it down her
brown neck. The girl bleated like a goat as Estève wiped her off,
his fingers inside her blouse. The guests lumberd to their feet as
the music began. Blaise had brought the fiddlers and Lurôt blew
his bagpipe. The sound skirled naked and hot through the de-

scending twilight.

At first the revelers stomped awkwardly. Some dropped out. Cavel shuffled into the lilac bushes and was sick. Estève drew his wife toward the hayloft, tittering. But soon the music seized the dancers by the nape of the neck and flung them into motion. They moved in a fume of cider and sweat, their hobnailed shoes threshing the ground. Dogs who had been burrowing in the rank garbage turned and scurried between the dancers' feet. Flies swarmed out of the hedges.

Blaise danced with harsh abandon, lifting his partner from the earth and whirling her in jolting arcs. The girl's body lashed back and forth yieldingly in his grip and his face was set in cruel spite. The farmhands danced close, grinding their haunches into the flaring skirts. Now and again they strode back to the ravaged tables to pour cider down their parched mouths. Lurôt blew without halt. Driven by the acrid notes, starlings skimmed back and forth across the roof.

Beltran danced alone with the stilted precision of an old man. He brought his knees up sharply and held his hands above his head. The other dancers clapped to the beat of his mincing step. Faster and faster. He closed his eyes dizzily but kept whirling. Suddenly he faltered like a wearying top and stumbled sideways into Blaise. Blaise thrust him back to the hub of the circle. Out of control, the drunken clerk spun from hand to hand. He sagged toward the ground but they heaved him about. His mouth was open and gasping.

"Stop them," said Danielle; "stop them."

Falk paid no heed. The scene filled him with loathing. Yet it was unreal, like a clamorous nightmare. He was afraid, but could not comprehend his own fear. A desire to escape from La Hurlette and even from Danielle beat strong inside him. But he sat riveted, leaning on his cane and letting the cold rise in his back.

Amid hoarse outcries the men put the cider on the floor and threw over the tables, clearing a wide space. The steaming air shook with their tread. Amélie's face appeared at the kitchen window. It was strangely white and she called out in protest, but her words were lost in the tumult.

"Let's go inside the house," said Danielle.

"Soon," said Falk. He scarcely knew what he meant. He was waiting for something to happen, something loathsome but of intimate concern to him. It was a feeling he had had once before, in those marshes near Smolensk. And he could not keep his eyes from the ash tree; its leaves seemed to grow thicker in the waning light.

The bounding couples had torn loose and all the dancers clasped hands in a single round. Glazed with drink and exertion, they swept on in wild orbit. Then the whiplash uncoiled. Before Falk could move, one of the young men had leaped over to Danielle, seized her by the wrist and whirled her into the circle. In the careening wheel her gown flashed like a scorched leaf. The blood ran heavy under Blaise's eyes and Nicole spun with her mouth agape.

The wind reared up without warning. It raked the farmyard with chill gusts. The haze scattered and the sky came down like lead. Large cold drops of rain splashed against the barn. The dancers wavered and one of the fiddlers began wiping his bow. Monsieur Raymond slipped away hurriedly. Falk rose with a surge of relief.

But Blaise yelled out: "One more dance! A bridal dance for the captain and his lady!" He came to Falk breathing hard: "Join our round. No man should let another dance with his bride. Not on his wedding night."

Falk stared into his red eyes. "I can't. You know that."

"Just once. A man can do anything if he tries hard enough. You've killed my brother and now you're taking my sister to bed. What's a little dance to a man like you? For old times' sake!"

Falk called to Danielle: "Let's go. You're getting drenched."

But Nicole barred his way: "Hold my hands. Come dance with me. You can't deny me that. It's so little to ask." She hammered at him like an enraged child. "I shall never beg anything of you again, I promise."

"Don't be crazy, Nicole; it's impossible for me to dance." But hands tugged at him on every side and a voice shouted: "*Bravo la Wehrmacht!*"

Nicole dragged him into the circle. Falk looked for Danielle, but those who surrounded him were strangers and had faces like

vacant masks. Lurôt had drawn close: he seemed to be blowing
a single screeching note. It cut to the bone like the cry of a
broken bird.

Falk strove to keep his balance but Nicole pulled him after
her and the dancers began treading their mad round. He at-
tempted to lunge out of the circle but it hemmed him in. As it
whirled past, Falk saw Danielle fling herself at the barrier of
arms and thrashing legs. He labored toward her and struck wildly with his cane, but the wall of bodies threw him back. He
stumbled and Nicole's hand slid from his grasp. He called desperately: "Help me, Nicole, help me!" But no one listened and
Blaise's face spun around him, contorted with avid fury.

Falk started falling and heard Danielle scream. Her voice was
coming closer and closer. He rose to meet it but the shoes kept
smashing into his face. A wave gathered before him, higher and
swifter than any he had ever imagined. It blacked out the whirling ash tree and Danielle's cry. Falk knew that the towering crest
was about to break and engulf him. But beyond the green howl
of water he glimpsed a trough of light. It was dim at first. Then
it rushed upon him with a brightness he could not endure.

The dancers melted away under the downpour, bearing Danielle to the house.

After a time, Terrenoire shambled out to look at the dead
man. He bent low gazing at his torn features. Blood was clot-
ting in the fine red hair. He knelt as if to guard his guest from
the rain, and spoke to him softly: "You came back too soon,
Monsieur Falk, too soon."

THE POET AND HIS CRITICS: IV

A Symposium on John Crowe Ransom's "Master's in the Garden Again" Edited by Anthony Ostroff

---

INTRODUCTION

We have here a new poem by John Crowe Ransom. Though it takes off from a poem written more than forty years ago, "Master's in the Garden Again" is not a revision, as our four discussions of it amply demonstrate; it is finally and fully new work, thus an occasion for which we are all to be grateful. Leonie Adams, Muriel Rukeyser, and W. D. Snodgrass, all themselves distinguished poets, have brought to the poem their experience and understanding, and to their critical comments Mr. Ransom has responded with a statement of his intent. In this situation, clearly, there are difficulties to be met—if indeed a poem is meant first to draw us from ourselves into its own special world, and then, at last, to refer us more deeply into *our* lives and the larger life within which they exist. Our essayists have seen to it that we do not stop short of the whole route. All of what they write—even by the arguments and protests their words may sometimes inspire in us—serves our sense of the poem and, beyond it, our sense of life. One cannot be impartial about such work—that is its genius and its beauty in the critical perspective, and perhaps it is above all for that combination of intelligence and conscience they have brought to their task that Miss Adams, Miss Rukeyser, Mr. Snodgrass, and Mr. Ransom all deserve our particular thanks.

ANTHONY OSTROFF

JOHN CROWE RANSOM:

Master's in the Garden Again*

(To the memory of Thomas Hardy)

i

Evening comes early, and soon discovers
Exchange between these conjugate lovers.

"Conrad! dear man, surprise! aren't you bold
To be sitting so late in your sodden garden?"

"Woman! intrusion! does this promise well?
I'm nursing my knees, they are not very cold.
Have you known the fall of a year when it fell?
Indeed it's a garden, but if you will pardon,
The health of a garden is reason's burden."

"Conrad! your feet are dripping in muck,
The neuralgia will settle in your own neck,
And whose health is it that catches an asthma?
Come in from foul weather for pity's sake!"

---

* Reprinted from *Selected Poems* (Rev. Ed.) by John Crowe Ransom, by permission of Alfred A. Knopf, Inc. Copyright 1962 by Alfred A. Knopf, Inc.

"No," says the thinker. "Concede. I am here,
Keeping guard of my garden and minding miasma.
You're lonely, my loony? Your house is up there.
Go and wait. If you won't, I'll go jump in the lake."

ii

And the master's back has not uncurved
Nor the autumn's blow for an instant swerved.

Autumn days in our section
Are the most used-up thing on earth
(Or in the waters under the earth)
Having no more color nor predilection
Than cornstalks too wet for the fire
And black leaves pitched onto the byre.

The show is of death. There is no defection.

iii

He will play out his mood before he takes food.

By the bob of the Power the dark skies lower,
By the bite of Its frost the children were lost,
Who hurt no one where they shone in the sun,
But the valiant heart knows a better part
Than to do with an "O did It lay them low,
But we're a poor sinner just going to dinner."

See the tell-tale art of the champion heart.

Here's temple and brow, which frown like the law.
If the arm lies low, yet the rage looks high.
The accusing eye? that's a fierce round O.
The offense was raw, says the fix in the jaw.
We'll raise a rare row! we'll heave a brave blow!

A pantomime blow, if it damns him to do,
A yell mumming too. But it's gay garden now,
Play sweeter than pray, that the darkened be gay.

MURIEL RUKEYSER:

This poem is a rewriting of another, much earlier poem: it is quite different from the first in many ways, although some of the phrases are kept. John Crowe Ransom has done a strange thing; he has made an extension and a transformation, even while the method is maintained. So that time and choice, which can bear the rhyme away, have with this poem borne it back again in a different life.

The poet has already been his own critic; and I, as reader, have been told what he thinks here, what he has preserved and what thrown away. Years after "Conrad in Twilight," its first life, the poem has taken on a second life whose meaning is based on—and contradicts—the first. "Master's in the Garden Again" speaks for a further stage of life. It is a declaration, and a celebration; it is offered to the reader as a transparency with a key. The transparency is here because we have that early matrix, much less in itself than this new poem, which Ransom describes as a "completely new version of the old and rather ignominious 'Conrad in Twilight'" in the Preface to his *Selected Poems*, which will have appeared by now, and whose proofs Knopf was good enough to send me. Ransom adds that his "greatest pleasure in preparing this edition came from this poem and one other." They mark a new period, after a long time without poems.

During the long gap there were essays; one of these, two rather, are the key to the poem, taken along with the dedication of "Master's in the Garden Again" to the memory of Thomas Hardy. The strength of the new poem is very close to the qualities of Hardy, Hardy old and seen by Ransom in "Old Age of an

Eagle," an essay which first appeared in the *New Republic* in 1952. These qualities, established by admiration and a kind of identity declared and built, will be in the poem as it climbs and rouses past its dripping scene. But that comes later—although it is invoked by the dedication.

The poem sets the scene at once; although "Conrad in Twilight" jumped straight into dialogue, now we are given autumn ("Evening comes early"), the exchange (that is, true dialogue) and the man and woman, the lovers in bonds, conjugate. In the old days, the woman leaped right in, nagging:

> Conrad, Conrad, aren't you old
> To sit so late in your mouldy garden?

This time, Conrad is called both "dear man" and "surprise" (well, perhaps *he* is not called surprise, perhaps it is the warning voice of nagging practicality that is surprised by her own thoughts, but I think Conrad is dear man, and surprise, as he is later thinker and master and champion). He is mood; she is "intrusion." But we know more about him, more about her, more about the garden.

She calls him "bold" here, and one can live with that.

What is his boldness?

In the beginning, it is simply to stay in his garden. The garden, with the man and woman in it, we know from our own depth. Far back among explications, the *Zohar* gives us the Garden of Genesis as Gad–Eden, the Garden of Delight which is the City of God. Here it is, sodden, particular, contemporary, gone to muck and the end of autumn. Nothing "promises well." It is not Eden; it has a house in it. It is waiting its blow, and its blow will surely come.

It is possible to be put off early in this poem by what seems like bumpiness, coyness, dated diction. Ransom himself has warned us of this in other poems by other poets. The music he claims is one he has described in the Hardy essay: he uses the folk line, or dipodic line, with its symmetry and a syncopation in a line whose musical expectation is so strong that the pause which can be produced is in itself strong, too. This is a clear and country music on which Ransom counts, and he has provided it with two chief sounds to carry the range of this wide-ranging poem: the long *ā* established in *exchange* and *late* and carried through to the last sound of the last line, and the long *ō* that begins with *bold* and *cold* and takes us to *blow* and all the variant *o*'s and *ow*'s sounding out toward the end.

The new poem keeps the name Conrad for someone who may be an invention or a friend. The name takes almost all its elements from the poet's own name. Conrad answers with his gloomy boding; in his first incarnation, he was nursing his knees in the cold, and now he declares to her that he is; he asks his question about the falling blow ("Have you known . . . ?" he asks, and goes on, not waiting for an answer, which indeed the woman does never make). And, as rational man, *he* answers her calling it "sodden garden" with

> "Indeed it's a garden, but if you will pardon,
> The health of a garden is reason's burden."

The sounds here are an echo of the crossed-out "Forest of Arden" whose wraith he has said he is sitting in, in the first version of this poem, a lifetime ago.

The woman answers his mention of health with a "womanly" cautionary rounding back to the question of his own health, and a

> "Come in from foul weather for pity's sake!"

Look at the first poem, "Conrad in Twilight." There is no woman here, although these questions are asked. Many of the hard words are kept, nagging words of deterioration, ill health, ills of which damp and decline are reminders, asthma, neuralgia, goading and horrid.

> "No," says the thinker . . .

and he begins to pile up on her his mood. She is called more than "intrusion," of course, she's called "my loony," and he knows her loneliness. She is to go back in the house and wait. And she knows what will happen if she doesn't. In his own humorous, querulous, last-gasp effort to go beyond his mood, he tells her: he'll jump in the lake.

That is the end of her. The end of the dialogue. The end speech.

From now on all we have is acted out. In the first "Conrad" it was a matter of tea and slipper and a blazing log at home. In the old poem, autumn was "teasing" and the poem ended with a described autumn.

Here, in part II of the new poem, we have another couplet setting the scene, which is the action of the man, a still, negative persevering in the face of what seemed to be only a warning of lateness, cold, damp, his own creakiness. But it darkens—

> Nor the autumn's blow for an instant swerved

and then the described autumn, as it was in the earlier poem,

> Autumn days in our section
> Are the most used-up thing on earth

and then the Biblical "or in the waters under the earth." Used-up is what the persevering is about, *that* is what she has been calling him under the names of solicitude, *that* is what he has been refusing to be, even when it looked as though he could only be by sitting there. The black wet tatters of the year are here. Beyond them

> The show is of death. There is no defection.

Now a curious thing happens. We are beyond the old poem, and beyond the old life. There is something that is used up, and the poet knows what it is. It is the old life itself. And there is something more. What comes next, in the bringing-together of gardens? What have these all turned into? What comes, once the show of death has been produced before us? It is produced, in full strength "no defection" and in full music, *show* being recognizable as a key sound in this poem.

Part III begins with a magic statement: "He will play out his mood before he takes food." He has put away the life of the house up there with its food, its comforts and its mood-breaking. This is to be carried beyond the end. The one line is comparable to the couplets with which the other parts of the poem have begun, but they are shortened here to the brief magic. As it is said, the spell breaks, the weather breaks, the tragedies of the innocent arrive. The verse stands up, and bravery stands up. No more the world of nursing and neuralgia—or, if they are there, they are not central to this scene.

The dialogue is between man and the Power. The Hardy Power, the cruel weather, *It* with a capital *I*, and *I* with a capital all there is to deal with It. The children are gone, fallen, dead by suicide because they are too "menny," anyway lost. And no more the querulous

> "O did It lay them low,
> But we're a poor sinner just going to dinner."

The heart itself is transformed, no longer tell-tale heart but

> See the tell-tale art of the champion heart.

Now the incantation takes up speed and action, the sound begins to swing,

> Here's temple and brow, which frown like the law.
> If the arm lies low, yet the rage looks high.
> The accusing eye? that's a fierce round O.
> The offense was raw, says the fix in the jaw.
> We'll raise a rare row! We'll heave a brave blow!

Feeling has now been dealt with by assertion, domesticated, as Collingwood says. Ransom has spoken of the metaphysical Powers arrayed against him"; here they are as one Power. The development of parallel feelings in this poem, no, conjugate feelings, lets me suspect that the wife has her chance for some parallel in the house, although it must come out of her "pity's sake" that works for his health as he sits out his mood for the health of his garden. There is her condemnation to the house, but he has come through; the garden's condemnation in the metaphor, although we know what winter is.

Ransom is not going to allow the metaphor to take over. His "that time of year thou may'st in me behold" is around him, being dealt with. But what happens? what is happening?

> A pantomime blow, if it damns him to do,
> A yell mumming too.

It has already "happened," though, in decision and in sound. And with the choice of the man, the garden has chosen. . . .

> But it's gay garden now,

and the acting out, the singing, the making, which has done it
to this garden, grants us a last invocation.

Play sweeter than pray, that the darkened be gay.

Here are the bravery, the irony, the honesty, the surprisingly
banal moments, the music—and the maudlin, daily, saving life
in Ransom's quickened poetry. I go back to early readings of his
poems. The books of poetry at home were the Bible and Shake-
speare, Longfellow and the sections in *The Book of Knowledge*.
Then I came to Untermeyer's anthologies and the living poets,
and then, afternoons after school, read on the stairs at O'Malley's
old bookshop in New York, the Oxford editions of poets, the
leatherette Modern Library, Mosher's finely printed paper books.
Began to buy books with first money at about the time "Two
Gentlemen in Bonds" came out, after the grace of "Chills and
Fever." The narrow books, with their dark backs and their designs. The dooms of the equilibrists, the gallantry of Captain
Carpenter, the harvesters, the girls. And the first poem of this
garden, after all this lifetime with its poems, is transformed to
the early and late of this second poem, with its darkness and
play, its ease of irony as the poet moves along, full (as he said of
Hardy) of "fierce folkish humor."

There are questions left. I left a friend's house the other day,
and the doorman spoke to me. I was going across the river to
read poems. "Oh, well, if it's poems," he said, "there's bound to
be lots of questions." While the questions come, here the poem
is—unswerving itself, in the poet's phrase "half mystical, perhaps half maudlin," saved by both and saving.

Afterthought: I am still haunted by what happens to the woman in the poem and to the vowels that deepen and deepen into
the undersounds of the climax.

W. D. SNODGRASS:

Our poets have a way of blooming late, often after a long
sterile period. We have exciting enough early works, splendid
last works, but little work of maturity—precisely that period

when we might have expected the greatest work. In their middle years our poets often cannot write at all, or, as a substitute for some wisdom we cannot find, will flee to theorizing, philosophy and literary dogmatism. Often, only the approach of death can shock us from the trance of our life; we come to terms with *it* more courageously. The artistic problems stem from the problem with love and passion.

The problem is a problem: only a fool would think he knew an answer. How could one be a first-rate artist without offending, deeply, those he most loves? First, by the mere offense of being first-rate. That, with the envy it arouses, quite commonly costs one those dearest to him. All differences, inequalities, seem unjust and odious. We have been encouraged to be feminine or childish, while our women have been encouraged to compete and to dominate. But like most executives, they dominate not through ability but through will—a quality often rising from envy at what one takes for a *lack* of ability in one's self. Every sign of ability in others will be a very real injury. And that injury is likely to be all the greater coming from an artist, since his life involves keeping open the passions, which may be neither humane nor loyal. Meantime, the violence and faithlessness of our passions are only likely to be increased by our desire to be dominated and diminished, our childishness, which resents any loved one and will use its own faithlessness as a subtle and civilized weapon.

Not that many of us would care to reinstate the *droit du seigneur,* or to go back to an age when the male was valued for a brute physical force which we abhor. Yet it certainly seems that we have carried horrid democracy a bit far. Since the great revolutions of the nineteenth century—the Industrial Revolution and the artistic and intellectual revolutions which accompanied it—there has been no masculine, ordering force worth fighting against. In the arts, as in society, we see aimless revolt followed by aimless revolt. After the women went, then the children; the dogs appear to have their revolt fairly well under way; the vegetables are likely next. Nothing is really produced, since these rebellions are directed against powers which do not exist, and carried out by those who are lacking in either ability or purpose.

We have half-men, half-women, half-adults, half-children, and nothing first-rate anywhere. It is not to be expected that the poets, any more than the rest of us, could escape the problem.

Cruel as this sounds, Hardy was probably the luckiest—his wife died while he had many years to lament, to record the fierce subtleties of their marital techniques, to learn how much she *had* meant, yet marry his secretary and go on with his poems. Tactless and proud as she was, his first wife had perhaps found a way to sacrifice herself into those poems so far greater (as she must really have known) than any she could herself write—a way to escape from, yet aid, a work too great to live with. This suggests both a nobility and a despair quite beyond anything Hardy credited her with, and quite beyond any reasonable demand.

Frost outlived his wife, yet for all his brilliance, was never able to make the reappraisal. Perhaps the struggle had gone too far, left too much wreckage and guilt. His earlier poems are the glory of our period—yet he never fulfilled their promise. If Cummings' feelings had reached their fullest at twenty-five, Frost's had reached theirs at forty. When he said "How awful, yet I must . . ." he was a poet; when he says "I must, since it's right . . ." he is only a danger.

Williams truly loved his wife, yet spent years trying to injure her. Then, however, he could come back to her. Few have his magnanimity, which could forgive even someone he had so deeply wounded. After years of sterile literary dogmatism, it is to his wife that he comes back in his last great poem, "Of Asphodel"— the flower that tells of his enduring love.

To Stevens, love must have been only another expensive ornament, like philosophy or aesthetic theory, to decorate an essentially meaningless world, another wreath for the abyss. In his old age, after *his* years of literary philosophizing, he comes back to no particular woman, but only to a "heavenly desired . . . sleek among the tintinnabula" who alone could offset the grayness of age and the shadow of trees like wrecked umbrellas. He returns to no garden, but to a greenhouse—now battered and in need of paint.

Thomas was perhaps the unluckiest, or the weakest. He had no middle age, much less whatever wisdom it might offer. He died recording the loveless lusts we associate with adolescence, the pure-sex-in-the-pants which appeals so to those with pure-sex-in-the-head. He does not lament his own age and loss, but his father's; he leaves his wife as ruined victor, to write what she can.

In Ransom we see something different from any of these—a man who has made a deep commitment and firmly stood by it, at whatever price. Whether we can be glad is beside the point. We must hold our peace before great dedication and the great loss that always may mean. There are gains, too—we have, now, a new poem just when we had given up hope for it. And it is a thoroughly remarkable poem—one that not only records this problem of love and creativity, but, in that very act, partially transcends it.

Hermann Broch (in his introduction to Rachel Bespaloff's book *On the Iliad*) defines the style of old age as an *abstractism* which impoverishes its vocabulary in order to enrich its syntactical relationships. It no longer collects the brilliant atoms of "world content," but rather expresses its relationships, its structure. Thus, though it tends to share the scientist's concern for abstract universal structure, its productions come closer to the abstractism of myth.

This seems apt, and a proper distinction between this and Ransom's earlier poems. This is a poem of relationships; it, as a result, invites commentary as the earlier poems never did. Those first poems quite defeat criticism—one can only point to them, with perhaps a few sentences of explication, and say, "See? He's done it again!"

Even this poem's initial technical problem is one of relationships—how to use a passage from the earlier "Conrad in Twilight," now that that poem's situation has come to have more meaning with the passage of time:

> Autumn days in our section
> Are the most used-up thing on earth
> (Or in the waters under the earth)
> Having no more color nor predilection
> Than cornstalks too wet for the fire,
> A ribbon rotting on the byre,
> A man's face as weathered as straw
> By the summer's flare and winter's flaw.

This, the ending of the original poem, was never quite satisfactory. In itself it is remarkable—few poets could have handled dactyls (or anapests) so fluently, placing extra accents so skillfully to avoid the deadly dactylic bounce. But coming at the end of "Conrad in Twilight," a light and breezy poem, and sinking it into a kind of depression and flat despair, the passage was shocking and never quite right.

Ransom's answer now is not to lessen the contrasts, but rather to make them more extreme. He surrounds his original death-dull passage with two passages of the gayest and brightest sights and sounds. He even marks the sections off with numbers so that we cannot miss the contrast. It is a little like the classical sonata form: the first section is a light and high-comical scolding match between husband and wife; the second, the more serious passage already quoted, which raises the spectre of death impinging on Conrad; the last section, tonally like the first, but with an underlying grimness, a dramatization of that "show" which "is of death." The last section is a little like one of those Mahler scherzi where everything is so splendidly gay but for that *memento mori,* that one sour clarinet; or like children in their Halloween costumes—gay and death-haunted, sacrificial.

Not that there is no attention to vocabulary and detail in the poem. Who else could have written that third line? After two regular dactylic lines to set the scene and tone, enter the wife:

"Conrad! Dear man, surprise! aren't you bold . . ."

So metrically canny, yet so humanly alive! There is so much wife in that line, one can hardly stand it. It is as if a whole flock of bright birds had burst into the room, quarreling for territories. Fluttering and fluting, affectionate and affected, maddeningly charming, the pitches rise, fall, slide, state incredible themes.

And once begun, this jocular brilliance never leaves the poem. Again, the husband's half-joking gruffness:

"Woman! Intrusion! Does this promise well?"

Or the continual play of echoes and sound effects: "sodden . . . garden . . . pardon . . . burden . . . guard of my garden." Or the constant hovering on the brink of absurd and delicious puns: "asthma . . . miasma."

Yet these local pleasures are not like the brilliance of vocabulary in Ransom's earlier poems. They are not meant to define this atom of experience, but to conflict with it. They must provide a gaiety to balance the tragic grimness of the poem's situation and theme, yet must never become too attractive in themselves.

The only thing in the poem much reminiscent of the earlier vocabulary is in the Latinism of "conjugate lovers," and I'm not sure but that it is a mistake. For me, at least, "eldering lovers," which one of the intermediate versions had in that place, is better. Most of Ransom's other revisions have tended to cut down the brilliance of the individual line so that the archetypical structure of the whole poem could more fully be realized. Consider these lines with their counterparts in the printed poem:

> Woman! intrusion! is this done well?
> . . . .
> Conrad your feet are dipping in muck,
> . . . .
> Come in to your ever and loving pipe
> . . . .
> So, my loony and only, my wanton and wife,
> You may take yourself off, a while, my dear.

It must not have been easy to give those up. Yet, here again, the gains are clear.

Consider the title: "Master's in the Garden Again." Master? What does not that mean? Of course, it's something a servant might say about the head of the household as she runs to report to her real master—that is, her mistress. Therein, one of the ironies. The master himself recognizes that he is scarcely master of the house:

> You're lonely, my loony? Your house is up there.

Again, by a fine ambiguity, "Master" is just the term we might apply to a child in the family. "The Master, Conrad" is someone very different from "Master Conrad." In his rage, the old man is less like Oedipus or Lear than like a wilful child intent on his play, refusing his mother's demands that he wear rubbers, that he keep warm and dry, that he eat his meals. Just as a child may feel that the only way to preserve its identity against a devouring mother is to refuse to eat. "No!—that proves I'm alive! I'll finish my game." And typically, in his helplessness, his only weapon against the woman is to damage himself: to stay out in the cold longer, or finally to throw himself in the lake.

Then, she'll be sorry. No question but that she would; or that *he* would be sorry if she didn't come down and ask him to come in. For she must be like the constantly importunate, constantly rejected mother—which is both a cause and an effect of his helpless rage. True, in one sense, Conrad is like an Old Testament prophet, a Lear, an Oedipus, raging against those forces which he has come to resemble and which will destroy him. In this sense, too, he is the Master. But we must first see him as an old man who plays the role of a child, who, in turn, plays the role of Lear or Oedipus.

The game in which he plays that role, of course, is Art. For he must also be seen as the master artist, the Maestro. If his "show is of death" yet the management of that show is "reason's burden." Conrad is "the thinker" on guard against "miasma" and his own "loony." And it is precisely in this area that his lady attacks him—suggesting that he hasn't sense enough to come in out of the damp.

Yet, for all its concern with reason, the poem is very much more about passion. In the first version of the poem, the garden was described as "the ghost of a Forest of Arden." Good enough: not only the place of nature and exile from human unkindliness,

> Here feel we but the penalty of Adam,
> The season's difference; as, the icy fang
> And churlish chiding of the winter's wind

but also the place where the young lovers meet and miss and make love. In the new poem, however, such predilections have been transformed almost entirely into something less threatening— rage. For the poem could scarcely have been written until that transformation was possible. Rage is more easily turned back against the self, or turned against those one sees as all-powerful or impregnable. Neither could the poem be written until the two antagonistic forces, death and woman, could be identified. One of these forces is introduced in each of the first two sections; in the last section, Conrad moves to action, but only because he can identify these two forces. This is clearest in

> By the bob of the Power the dark skies lower,
> By the bite of Its frost the children were lost,

As a Limiting Power upon Life, woman and death are one. Just as it bobs, so she bobs down from her house, lowering, and calling her children home. Naughty, they will play out their games —fierce and grotesque games—the games of Art and Prophecy— games which demonstrate the blankness of the world which has formed and controlled them. "The accusing eye? that's a fierce round O." And that eye, that rage, looks high—to her house or to the skies, to the Power which dwells there and has defeated the old man, laid his arm low, and now scolding affectionately, calls him home to a final surrender. This is only an inversion of our common tendency to see death as a mother, the grave as a womb.

Just as Oedipus' ultimate identity with his Fate is never seen in any surrender on his part, but rather in an implacable rage which shows him to be essentially like that implacable Fate and basically part of it, so here Conrad's refusal to enter the house, his insistence on acting out his self-directed rage and accusation, proclaim his essential oneness with the Powers. His temple and brow frown like the law; it is clear that his laws are woman and death. In that sense, there is no defection, all appearances to the contrary. If he, momentarily, refuses to come in, he will eventually go and be glad enough for the messenger's visit. It shows a constant, almost divine concern for his well-being. And his rage shows, finally, his lack of freedom from her.

Stanley Kunitz recently reminded us of Goethe's dictum that all Art lies in Limit, reminding us himself, however, that the artist must always try those limits to the utmost. No doubt most of us accept too readily limits which comfort us emotionally, a world conformable to a childish demand for a universe much concerned with our welfare. Still, who would accept a world of open rage, of unlimited passion. If we are too childish to be Oedipus, we are also too compassionate. Though this dilemma has itself limited the size and scope of this poem, yet the poem has defined, at the same time, that dilemma—the gain and loss, the passion and compassion, those stools between which life occurs. This seems to me a triumph.

So, in the Garden of his Art, the Master plays out a late performance; one equally composed of protest and reconciliation. For if House and Garden are separated, both still stand. If Master and Woman will never be closer, they will never be farther. If the Gardens have been long shut, we villagers must know there have been sufficient reasons. Today, Master's in his verse patch again and his formal gardens are open to the public; who can be less than grateful?

LEONIE ADAMS:

The poem with its broken spacings has not quite the look of a Ransom work. The opening couplet is his unmistakably, in its every inflection. Then, for me, with the abrupt third line the impression of divergence deepened (despite gathering echoes and the recognition of the splendid autumnal passage in Section II) and has survived a thorough reading and comparison of the poem with its prototype, "Conrad in Twilight." From that earlier lyric, which remained unchanged from *Chills and Fever* to the 1948 selection, the present poem borrows its hero's proper name, details and certain phrases relating the sodden (there "mouldy") garden to his person and ailing years, most of Section II, and the theme of age confronting a show of death. Common to both is the first repercussion of the theme and tactic of the poems: to appear to treat Conrad's lingering in this confrontation as an exasperating folly.

Nevertheless one must end by considering "Master's in the Garden Again" not as a revision or enlarged version, but as another poem. Theme and hero have been simultaneously particularized and extended in figure, the garden has taken on a stronger metaphoric dimension. And nevertheless, "Conrad in Twilight," even if the author chooses to discard it, will for a time haunt

many readers' response to the new poem. At this reading I judge
the latter to be the more interesting and elaborate of the two, and
the more baffling. Ears tuned to them may miss in it the continu-
ing felicities of tone in favorite Ransom poems, and it is to the
relative disappearance of the centering voice (for the voice here
is more variously and directly mimetic) that I attribute the new
poem's peculiar open-endedness among so many which have been
notable for controlling equivocations discreetly.

A voice speaks throughout "Conrad in Twilight" and is
one variant on the author's uses of such a controlling voice. For
it would be a mistake to assume because we recognize this voice
as "his" in its combination of personal rhythm, metric habits,
and verbal sensibility, that it is identically employed in different
poems. Mr. Ransom has said that he considers the dramatic monologue the *central* poetic form, and this is one of his critical
dicta rather subtly related to his practice. He has not made the
dramatic monologue in the usual sense his characteristic form.
But the voice which speaks his poems is always crucial to their
effects, and is only deviously the poet's own. Like the fictional
point of view it is maneuvered, in its more contracted space, to
lead us through a series of perspectives to the essential apprehen-
sion. These perspectives may suggest roles, attitudes of partici-
pants, may be only the inflections of the unsaid. Sometimes, as
with the fictional device, the point of view becomes the real pro-
tagonist.

What we have in "Conrad in Twilight" is someone ruminat-
ing the elderly Conrad's ruminatings (and situation) and en-
forcing their savor upon the reader. "Conrad, Conrad, aren't you
old" it begins, "To sit so late in your mouldy garden?" and
goes on with an odd suggestion of mimicking the accents of a
proper and prudent scolding in of the old gentleman; and then
again of those same accents mingled with his own promptings
(or temptations) to flee his misery where

> The log on Conrad's hearth is blazing
> Slippers and pipe and tea are served,
> Butter and Toast are meant for pleasing!

Or is all this the voice of rage and outrage at the flimsy intru-
sions of solace? The reader has not many clues to Conrad. He

will suppose him to have been given to gallantry, though perhaps not much more than is common since the knees he "nurses" are here

> . . . too rheumy and cold
> To warm the wraith of a Forest of Arden

and there is a ribbon (rather incongruously) rotting on the byre of the last passage. The most direct statement of his situation follows on the opening quoted above, and is a telling one:

> And I think Conrad knows it well

says the voice, with an eerie sardonic note. The voice that speaks this first portion (three stanzas) of the poem, though so versed in the matter, is an elusive one. The innocent reader may begin to read in a tone of tender chiding, and find he cannot keep it up; he is receding to a maximum distance of empathy. The strains of feeling in the last word of the third stanza:

> Still Conrad's back is not uncurved
> And here's an autumn on him *teasing*.

"Teasing" is odd for autumn, especially the autumn about to be served up, one of those savage understatements (like the "vexed" in "Bells for John Whiteside's Daughter"), or euphemisms which are directed toward the furies of pity.

In the final stanza, "Autumn days" (cf. Section II of our new poem), the speaker gives up slyness, shifts of tone in the limited sense, becomes the most impersonal voice of all, lost in what it says—although phrasing and rhythm here are more barely idiomatic than elsewhere. The change is abrupt, and structurally the strongest thing in the poem—as if the first stanzas had been given only to afford us this sense of being brought up against the scene without recourse. The scene and its occupant are unchanged. Simply, they are now *seen*. Or, the voice has dropped its sham distance to transport us to the intimate position of no or absolute distance.

These lines are truly remarkable in their bareness of means. Two or three properties for the seasonal desolation, its extension in an illusive phrase ("the waters under the earth," which has also its flavor of a way of speech, a habit of feeling) and we have the immediate garden and its suggestion of the very limbo of matter's descent; the balance of "color" (an obvious generalization for the sensible) and "predilection" (the unexpected, concentratedly precise term for the ground in nature of the human) and there begins the assimilation to this scene of the man. A final image of a now impersonalized Conrad closes this movement and the poem:

> A man's face as weathered as straw
> By the summer's flare and the winter's flaw.

The face is not quite the man, but is an expressive attribute. Flare and flaw will do very well to speak for him inwardly. It will be a poor reader who is not respectful of the poem's reticence here, and ready to accept its propriety as one of those proprieties which it is the business of tone to prepare readers for and to sanction. Why then is this poem not one of Ransom's best?

Judgments such as that just implied will vary, and cannot be fully explained. Is it that the poem as conceived would be a subject more fruitful for a painter? It is not of course treated pictorially. Mr. Ransom has always been as sparingly descriptive as a poet can be, although he has been masterly at suggesting the visual in its repercussions. One way of indicating the impression of certain of his poems would be to say that such and such a pencil, penetrating at one stroke the actual of the grotesque and the harrowing, or of the ludicrous and the touching, could have drawn the mourners at this bed, the guests at this wedding. It is true that the best remembered of these evocations are given off in the course of a narrative movement, or the unfolding of a situation, and Conrad's is a still image. But then the author's poems *are* largely narrative, and the image postulated in "Painted Head," though so volatile in the movements of being it engenders, is yet more static than a man in a garden. Nor am I content to ascribe everything to the naked shift of tone (and metric) in the last lines. Yet this shift and Conrad's immobility, and still more, his lack of definition do contribute to a disrelation between the first stanzas of the poem and the final portion. The detail of the earlier lines recedes and we are left too much with Age and Death. The "general" of the poem is not fast in all its particulars as it is in comparable pieces: "Dead Boy," "Bells for John Whiteside's Daughter."

I have set down all this concerning "Conrad in Twilight" because it constituted some sort of clue for me to the novel manner of the new poem. "Master's in the Garden Again" is concerned with some of its author's chief themes of experience and of speculation. It exploits, formally, the play of the comic and the pathetic, the terms of the domestic piece and the fable. But it manages all these in a way for him unprecedented. almost obverse to his usual practice. And though it ends by raising other questions, it begins by settling those raised by "Conrad in Twilight."

Thus, if the directions of mockery there were puzzling and unplaceable they are here embodied and patent. Conrad does act and speak, and at last is spoken for. The alternation of sections is reinforced and fully structural. The metric is the old native metric, easier to accommodate to the transposed passage. Mr. Ransom has used this metric before, but chiefly in its more rocking movement and for one kind of effect. Here it is put through more paces, from the doggerel alliterative to the broken and piercing, and with the sprinkled rhymes is made to change qualitatively from part to part, and this is very adroit. And lastly, if in the earlier poem the central voice (and so tone) did not work altogether sustainingly, its role here is indeed diminished, intermittent.

From one view this poem is an abbreviated example of qualitative form, or musical form, a composition of rhythmic variations. Other examples that come most easily to mind are enlargements of the dramatic monologue: the speaker offers us such a range of experience, image and reflection that he is not too much with us as subjective sufferer nor too much thinned to mere mind, yet it would be hard to conceive the unity of such poems without him. Here we have something different. The speaker is only a chorus-prologue-narrator presenting us with a scene, interlude, and dumb show.

There is something droll and folkish, crudely and immemorially traditional suggested, not only in this one-man chorus of all work, but in the poem's whole manner: something stilted and puppetlike in the opening colloquy; raw in the touch of the grotesque upon the painful in the pantomime; touching in the disjunctive strains of chorus.

The chorus is the most sophisticated poet and has the longest part and best lines. After the terse prologue the dialogue scene of Section I is comedy of manners and the stylized puppet-shrilling is an overtone of this. It is comedy of manners at a point where disguise frays indecently, and we hear the nervous archness of the woman's opening phrases break down into the grindingly inept, and the husband's irony snappishly overdone, edging into the vicious.

Is it the stock character frame (which I may have invented) which makes me see this pair so readily as man, woman, Adam, Eve, as levels or masks of reason? Woman is not here, as in other of the author's poems, the tenderly deluded, innocently wounded sensibility. As the underside of solicitude she embodies rather petty, greedily limited, practical reason. The action is to banish her temporarily so that a superior reason may find itself. Man is lordly in his unconscious assumption of himself as reason ("The health of a garden is reason's burden") and achieves absurdity in enunciating its dictates ("minding miasma"). The chorus-narrator in a thin aside calls him "the thinker" as in Section III he mocks him with "Master." (This begins to remind us of "Old Man Playing with Children," in which folly or second childhood becomes wisdom; but the present poem could not contain the willful extravagance of statement there, nor, in its different management resolve and poise implications so lightheartedly.)

Despite the impartiality of the comic vein, the reader is with the woman's banishment, and ready, as in the earlier poem, for the preparation of silence—indeed, readier so that the effect of the break is deepened. The opening lines of Section II (which adds only these and a final line of equal gravity to the transposed passage) are very good in giving duration to this silence. Time has passed. (Here one begins to feel a thickening sense of parody, as of our truncated, overburdened structures, fragmentations, dislocations, etc.) During the intermission what has happened? Peripety, a whole tragic action ("the show is of death"), recognition on the part of the hero, or just the off-stage violence? In this section the chorus is traditionally enough describing the scene. But the scene as the order of nature is the antagonist and, as omnipotent, stands over the hero's defeat. We are now where we were at the end of "Conrad in Twilight," except that that poem is complete, and a page break here would not deceive us. For here the unresolved lingers from the impassive opening couplet of the section. "And the master's back has not uncurved" bears that curved back with some ring of pride but means too a shying as far back from acceptance as the recesses of infant omnipotence. The magic, or perhaps prayer, didn't work: "Nor the autumn's blow for an instant swerved." However, the hero is sitting out the moment of truth and we expect more of him. What? The happy, comic ending, heroic action, epiphany, food for choric wisdom? The elements so far given work on us "teasingly" (though perhaps only, or chiefly if we have been brought to feel the mock-heroic, parody sense), and we could look to have any of these in a back-handed fashion. Perhaps that is what we do find, a little of each, in just that fashion, inside out, upside down.

That Conrad will trot in to supper is comic ending, reversed by coming first, especially since the preceding half line foretells his action and undercuts it as sham "play" and its ground as "mood." For epiphany, then, we would next have reason in truer guise as moral sensibility and human champion. The chorus narrator in this crucial section splits up. Spoken as from within we have offended justice, a snatch of poignance, the pity of it. Then the pantomime, a heroic action, seen, is travestied in doggerel and with the insulting indulgence we have for a child's tantrum, and now too the inward voice of content is made bluster. An image hovers above all this, grotesque, apoplectic, rigor mortis, for the accusing rage. Epitaphy? The last phrases are more true chorus and resolving. But how can we believe in this gay garden? Not as in the "olive garden for the nightingales" of the poet's "Painted Head."

For one thing the sequence grief-pathos, rage, gaiety is emotionally strange. It would be easier to enter into this sequence through accepting the literal image simply: a man in the defect of age, transported to excess by a frost-bitten garden, purged in the frail round of senescent humors.* On the other hand, I should find the whole burden of the piece impossible to load upon Conrad as Conrad. This sense would for me put "Master's in the Garden Again" about out of the canon as all belabored to one harshness.

The last reversal, in the reading I incline toward, is this: *we* recognize the hero. He resolves his plight by a rudimentary mime. Other redemptive play-forms, (manners and ceremony, ritual religion) which the author has set beside the play-form of art show in this late garden as shrunken and malformed. We read the poem then as fable: a fable of the straits to which a noble art is fallen, and including in its parody aspect ("Have you known the fall of a year when it fell?" and more not here adumbrated) reminders as well of that art's self-conscious burden of history, and feeble origins "where all the ladders start."

As fable it is a wry one, with parody pervasive and reaching to the exegesis it prompts. But its poet-hero, with his fist-shakings at heaven, is after all an embittered romantic, remote from the classic temper and the olive garden which "Painted Head" (also, though so brief, managing a historic-modern perspective) at last postulated and celebrated. And, as fable it differs from any other of Ransom's poems developed figuratively. In others the literal level, clearly figurative and fabulous, returns us to the tenor of the actual by concentrating, enhancing and ordering the moral dimensions of behavior and of fact. Here, the literal level (Conrad) seems actual and solid, and as vehicle diminishes the human reach it adumbrates. Yet as vehicle the poem holds him in more acceptable relations than merely as old man.

And what of the dedication? Hardy made the garden the scene of a number of late poems. These were in the mode of pure pathos, and often achieved the pure dignity of pathos in the tragic scheme. The words "rage" and "gay" are apt to remind us of another poet of old age. I take it that these poets are invoked (if indeed both are) as geniuses of the shore, beyond the floods which would roll old fellows and old forms in the dust.

---

*I am omitting here the ambiguous use of "children," preferring, for a confluence of reasons, to take its sense as of "babes" in "Miriam Tazewell."

JOHN CROWE RANSOM:

Three poet-critics have looked hard at my first poem. I mean the first made by my present Self, who has grown out of the several other Selves during the years of no poetry; made with all that awkwardness when one tries for the first time to fashion some difficult kind of thing. I am indebted to these critics because they have said what they thought about the poem, with sincerity and care. What can a poet do without critics to advise him what he is doing? And without critics to pass over in silence some of his favorite passages and by that silence tell him that he has not done what he thought he was doing? I can imagine that this latter testimony is one that happens often to poets who try to do only wonderful things, and discover from the general silence that poetry for them is tense, terse, and jerky, and that they do not address themselves to the general intelligence. It is well that this is a first poem.

Miss Rukeyser has gone right through the poem, defining the drift of its successive movements, and finally, with her unusual power of sympathy, responding approvingly. She cheers the author's spirits. There is a word of caution at the end, to say that one never finishes with the study of a poem, but no direful threat that other questions which may be raised about the poem cannot be answered so favorably.

Mr. Snodgrass has made a fighting defense of my poem, attending specifically to the vocabulary and verbalisms which he finds generic to the poet advanced in age, and happy to the point of overstatement at the success of the old poet trying his hand again. I have not met with so complete a champion turning up so unexpectedly. It makes me glad, and wary. As to the woman's deep involvement in the story, I keep thinking, How right he is there; he recognizes the bond that unites the man and the woman, the garden and the house, in perfect keeping with the author's understanding. One thing is missing in his study: the question of the success of the man's peculiar pantomime at the end, which is exactly the trouble-spot of the whole poem. Is it worth the bluster and the bother it has cost him, even if at last it can take place in the secrecy of his garden? Is it either probable or possible? Perhaps in the time and the space Mr. Snodgrass did not get round to it, but I cannot afford to think so.

Miss Adams is one of the most acute and intensive critics we have, very sure and exacting in testing the suitability of the verbal phrase and the detail of the action. Her own verse is a rare achievement for our time in its lyric purity. Ever so well she knows the few best of my early poems, and inclines to hold this late poem officially to their standard of performance. She stops fastidiously on the frequent harshness of the moral tone, the "broken spacings" and violent shifts in the narrative, the grotesquerie, the childishness of the final action, the comic note that may not have been intended. But she is willing not to make her judgment final, and that determines me to take plenty of time in coming to my own judgment. Her voice in this group is the indispensable complement to the others.

I thank especially Mr. Ostroff, our moderator, who accepted the poem while it was still unfinished, then assembled these bright and right persons to appraise it, and now asks me not to stint my reply in depth or in length.

My remarks will run at random. They will have to do wholly with some of the author's intentions, not his successes, about which I do not yet have an opinion.

The title which I gave to the poem (in place of the "Conrad in Twilight" which topped the little old poem), and the dedication to Thomas Hardy, jumped into my consciousness simultaneously out of the memory of a slight but touching poem of his entitled "The Master and the Leaves." Its next-to-last stanza finishes the leaves' complaint, and the last stanza gives the master's reply:

III

We are turning yellow, Master,
    And soon we are turning red,
And faster then and faster
    Shall seek our rooty bed,
All wasted in disaster;
    But you lift not your head.

IV

—"I mark your early going,
And that you'll soon be clay,
I have seen your summer showing
As in my youthful day;
But why I seem unknowing
Is too sunk in to say."

My title therefore became "Master's in the Garden Again"; as
he often was. But the date line of the Hardy poem is 1917. At
that time the poet was too dispirited by the World War, and
perhaps too tired, to spend himself reiterating his old defiance
against the Power that knows no special providence for Its crea-
tures; he can only tell the leaves politely that he has seen what
is happening to them. But it would have been indecent for me
to pretend that Hardy is the master in the garden of my poem.
The master—and hero—is still Conrad; and if there is any interest in this item I will say that to the best of my knowledge I
had chosen that name, in the early 1920's, because it had been
the pen name of a brooding and intellectual Pole who wrote
novels, and I happened to have been born in a town called
Pulaski, about sixty miles from where he wrote. At any rate I
would have preferred to have Hardy in my garden as he had
been much earlier than the time of his own poems about the
garden; let us say between the conclusion of his novels in the
early 1890's and the turn of the century. That was when he was
close on sixty years old, full of vigor as I suppose, and getting
himself powerfully engaged upon his theological misadventure.
The evidences would be in the astonishing epic drama of *The
Dynasts,* and many small poems both before and after. I cannot
deny that my imagination, while I was working on the present
poem, would sometimes picture for me the aging but not yet
aged Mr. T. H. sitting drooped on a wet stone in a prospect of
fallen leaves, and maintaining his posture with only the slightest
variation while he talked with his wife Emma, then brooded a
while, and finally in his solitary rage made his play against the
Immanent Will. It was a fleeting and pleasant vision but not
suitable to Hardy's great dignity; though I could ask myself,
Who is likely to know the peculiar habit or the ritual by which

even a great poet raises and resolves his fury?

I must talk about that first stage in the poem, where Conrad seems harsh to his wife when she interrupts his revery. One of my governing motives in this composition was to try for certain formal effects, which would be prosodical effects, all through the poem. I felt that the four-beat folk line, with its perfect two-plus-two symmetry, was capable of great versatility, so that in the three movements there might easily be as many effects. In the first movement the lines are end-rhymed as is common, but in irregular stanzas which assemble themselves in a very arbitrary way. That is to say that at the beginning I did what was quite irregular, but justified it by the characters I attributed to the man and the woman having their dialogue, and expected my readers to follow me though these had not been revealed. Conrad is a poet and his wife is not; he rhymes easily, but she has no knack for it. So the naughty man means to hear out her un-rhymed lines, then cap them with a group of lines that supply rhyme-mates for hers, and for good measure some rhymed lines entirely his own. That is why her first address in two lines end-ing with *bold* and *garden* is followed by his stanza of five lines ending with *well, cold, fell, pardon, burden;* two separate rhym-ings for her *garden.* Her next sally has four lines ending with *muck, neck, asthma,* and *sake.* His reply is to assume that *muck* and *neck* may be put to her credit as lame rhymes (a little of his art having rubbed off on her) though probably their near-rhyming is perfectly accidental. He replies with four lines ending in *here, miasma, there,* and *lake.* The insult of the rhymes looks very rude of him; yet I thought of it as one of the conventions of their dialogue whenever they were having an argument. But in my obstinate economy of words I blundered here. I should have supplied an ampler leisure, and more and successively clearer examples of the rhyme game.

I had taken my cue from the charming but sophisticated French poet Jules Laforgue, to whom Mr. Eliot's prose criticism and early imitations had introduced me, and started off by trying to outdo him. But there are some genuine locutions in Laforgue's style. One of his best inventions was to match an intellectual man with the woman of his heart who was a sentimentalist; so that if the woman, for example, asks the man if he loves her still, he may reply with some completely irrelevant wisdom beyond her head. The invention works as a convention; it does not keep Laforgue's heroes from showing their real gallantry in action, when the occasion arises. Similarly Conrad, as when his first speech to his wife begins with a fierce pair of exclamations: "Woman! intrusion!" Or when he calls her his loony; this is mock brutality, well understood between them. He is too polite to tell her to "go jump in the lake," and only threatens to do it himself if she will not leave him now; nor is she alarmed over that, as if she has heard it many times before. It is only his final word that closes the argument; the master speaking. And on the other hand there seem to be some equally unflattering conventions of speech on her part. Conrad's two exclamations were only replies to those on her tongue when she entered the garden. "Conrad! dear man, surprise!" Indeed her playful language is more resented by Mr. Snodgrass, who is a man, than Conrad's. Possibly the convention which is her best weapon of attack is to assume the role of protecting Conrad's frail health, when it may well be that his health is very good, and never in his life has been impaired by neuralgia nor asthma. It is clear that I damaged my poem by making it take off from the ill-laid foundations of the old fragment, where the speaker or speakers make derogations against his failing age. In the early piece somebody says, "Aren't you old / To sit so late," etc. But in whipping the new poem into shape I changed *old* to *bold;* a word better befitting a hero. At the same time I changed one of the new phrases I had entered, *eldering lovers* becoming *conjugate lovers,* for two reasons probably: to keep the pair from seeming too senile for their duties, and—as Mr. Snodgrass has made me aware—because the latter word seemed more important as a precise and structural specification, eloquent only in the expectations it permitted.

Thinking of the rowdy persiflage of my conjugate lovers as a sporting and comic feature, I have the sense that their life together is good. I like to think of their marriage as still real, in the lawyers' sense of the word, meaning physical. Yet all will not be lost as they grow old. The diminishing desires of the flesh will be compensated by bonuses of extra companionship and affection. When they are not together, the garden and the house will be their respective spheres. But after the man's turn in the garden his appointment will be in the house. Mr. Snodgrass has said this almost precisely.

Now I skip over the second movement, which is only a static scene described by the author, noting only the last line: "The show is of death. There is no defection." The death mentioned means to refer to that of the leaves, of whom not one has survived, though they were the children "Who hurt no one where they shone in the sun." The author did not want to suggest the universal mortality to which Conrad himself, and all of us, are liable, and for which Conrad, like most of us at his time of life, is prepared. But that would be another poem. It is the dead leaves that matter now, and they are what he sorrows for. In this poem it is in the third movement that he rouses himself as the leaves' champion, and girds himself for heroic action. But he must fight for a lost cause; the leaves are gone already. So he will raise his hand and voice against the blind and brutal Power to punish him. Yet there is the most abject absurdity here. Conrad has no chance of hurting, nor of reaching, nor even of finding the awful Power; and Conrad knows it. Human justice is meted out ordinarily by tiny men against a tiny man, or a tiny hero against a tiny villain, but this case is different. In what fashion can Conrad play the hero even in his own estimation if he has to proceed against the unknown Power? He has been careful not to expose his enterprise to the public view. But another recourse suggested itself to the not impartial author.

The prosodical variation in this movement consists in abandoning the rhyme of lines with each other, and making them rhyme within themselves, the fourth or end beat with the second or middle beat. The rhyming becomes more immediate, therefore more audible; and more frequent too; altogether making perhaps for a richer music and a livelier substance. Furthermore, the lines fall into their proper groups structurally, logically, and we have the equivalent of the free paragraphs of a prose composition, or one in blank or free verse.

Now Conrad can take no real action against the Enemy, though I suppose we are all aware by now that he is going to perform a symbolic action which amounts only to pantomime. He will frown and look fierce, and grit his teeth, and at last he will raise his clenched fist toward Heaven and give a muffled yell of defiance. But let us not discount this operation in advance. What if the author will describe it in some special and stylized manner; is there a chance of his keeping the reader's attention and making the thing seem credible though strange? We know how much is done by sheer stylization when the storyteller would have us believe in his unsubstantial ghost, or some phantasy with many characters. But each case is too particular to generalize it. In the five lines of the pantomime where we see Conrad's features working in silhouette, and even in the final three lines which follow in the author's official voice, we have a very special prosodical variation upon the prosodical movement which I have described. All the sixteen rhyme-places, half in the middle and half at the ends, are supplied with long open vowels, which have no consonants after them or else silent consonants. Sixteen rhyming syllables, yes, sixteen monosyllables, fill those places, and show six different rhymes based on the following words, which are not given in the order in which they appear: *law, low, high, now, do, gay.* It used to be the understanding among poets that any two long open syllables at the right places would be construed as rhyming, but that is unnecessary here, where each one can find a rhyming partner, sometimes more than one. I shall not tell of the pain this pattern required of its composer, nor the joy when it began to work out. But it is pertinent to say that the authorial imagination works in two ways at the same time, and that the severity of the requirement produced finally lines that not only answered to the prosody but were more striking and unexpected than they might have been in the substance.

I do not know if the pantomime passage succeeded. But it pleased me that when it was finished the author's little epilogue or last word came into its three lines almost instantly, without sacrificing the pattern or the pertinence:

> A pantomime blow, if it damns him to do,
> A yell mumming too. But it's gay garden now,
> Play sweeter than pray, that the darkened be gay.

The garden is gay, if it can be gay, because the hero has performed his action, though it was only a symbolic action, in a sort of grand style, making something out of a barren occasion. And in the last line, with "Play sweeter than pray," the author has imagined himself as on the track of an incipient law for poetry, a way for it to distinguish itself from theology when theology has failed the poet: to play the thing that we cannot pray.

So Conrad is purged and away to the house which expects him.

ANTHONY OSTROFF, whose poetry and fiction have appeared in a number of magazines, is the author of *Imperatives,* and teaches at the University of California in Berkeley. JOHN CROWE RANSOM, poet, critic and for many years editor of the *Kenyon Review,* is the author of *The World's Body* and other books; his *Selected Poems* first appeared in 1945. MURIEL RUKEYSER has not only published poetry, but biographies and children's books as well. Her latest volume of verse is *Poems, Selected and New.* W. D. SNODGRASS, poet and critic, teaches English at Wayne State University in Michigan. His book, *Heart's Needle,* won the Pulitzer Prize for Poetry in 1960. LEONIE ADAMS, poet and educator, has received, among other awards, the Bollingen prize in poetry and the Shelley Memorial Award. Her most recent book is *Poems, a Selection.*